The Big Dish

The Big Dish

The Fascinating Story of Radio Telescopes

Roger Piper

Illustrated with photographs
and with diagrams by Felix Cooper

Harcourt, Brace & World, Inc., New York

First American edition

Library of Congress Catalog Card Number: 63-7890
Printed in the United States of America

Title page photograph, Keystone

Acknowledgments

I should like to express my thanks to Mr. Reginald G. Lascelles, Special Assistant to Sir Bernard Lovell at Jodrell Bank, for the help given to me on the telescope site and for his suggestions, later adopted in the text.

The facts in Chapter 10 are based on an article, "The Control and Tracking of Satellites in Deep Space" by Mr. Lascelles, and I am grateful both to the author and to the Central Office of Information in London for permission to use them.

I am also indebted to Mr. Henry Charles Husband, B. Eng., M.I.C.E., M.I. Mech. E., for information on the design and construction of "The Big Dish."

Roger Piper

Contents

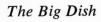

The Big Dish

1

First Glance at the Big Dish

To the east lies the Pennine mountain range — the backbone of England — to the west, the Welsh hills, and, in the center, a plain covered with cornfields, meadows, oak trees, and an occasional farmhouse.

Here, at Jodrell Bank Experimental Station, before an audience of cows, sheep, and a few privileged humans, stands the world's largest completely steerable radio telescope. They call it the Big Dish.

The Big Dish reminds different people of many different things. A writer in the London *Daily Mail* compared it to a giant begging bowl held out to collect knowledge. To others, it has a personality. Certainly it can stare straight at one or turn its back or look up at the sky for inspiration.

To me, when seen from afar, with all its girders hidden by the trees and its glance turned sideways, it seems a little like a pale gray flower—an anemone or windflower.

At first you are not certain how to drive up to this wonder of the world, standing as it does in the middle of green
fields. Eventually you turn down a byroad until you reach

A close-up of the Big Dish at Jodrell Bank, Cheshire, England, taken while the telescope was tracking the first Russian satellite. (Ken Lambert, Camera Press, London)

a notice telling you to "Keep Out." That (if you have an appointment) is where you drive in — along a winding single-track macadam lane for about three hundred yards

— and there you are, in front of a modern streamlined red-brick building — the brains of the telescope.

Seen close to, the structure, towering up almost to the clouds, is as inspiring as a temple, and perhaps the men who work the telescope were still a little in awe of it when they first began saying to each other, "After all, it's only like a very big dish."

The telescope may be looking straight up to the zenith, which is what astronomers call the point straight overhead. Or it may be moving gently and slowly to point at some unseen radio constellation in the blue sky, a radio source that, for our eyes, had been blotted out either by the brilliance of the sun or by the clouds.

In any case, the telescope is a sight worth seeing.

Professors and graduate students from all over the world have come to Jodrell Bank — from the United States, from Russia, Japan, India, Norway, and so on. Graduates who have already passed through a university and taken their degrees and who have, perhaps, a string of initials after their names fight to be allowed to spend three to five years with the Big Dish, which has nothing to do with eating.

They realize that perhaps within a few years, it will tell us more than was ever known before about the present state of the universe and about its history more than six thousand million years ago.

A "day" in the life of this giant radio telescope begins at midnight. All is quiet in the controller's office, from which the movements of the telescope are directed. The lights are carefully shaded so that the single operator can see clearly the whole telescope standing in the fields about two hundred yards away.

No one is supposed to disturb the controller in his room — and even the scientists working on the same problem rarely telephone him to ask questions. The readings on the instrument dials in the control room are watched by a television camera, which sends on the information to screens in the research laboratory, so that there is no need for anyone to enter the control room itself in order to read them. As a further defense against interruptions, the information received by the telescope is kept clear of the control room. It all goes to a separate laboratory — the information room — elsewhere in the building.

The information room contains a teleprinter directly connected with the United States so that scientists at Jodrell Bank can hear the latest news of U. S. satellites — some of which carry British equipment. Next door to the research laboratories and information room is a small lecture hall.

So much for the offices. Now for the telescope itself.

Of course, if it is already in use, no one is allowed to go out and clamber around the bowl. And rightly, too. Suppose, for example, someone was at work painting the dish when it started to tip? Or suppose someone was repairing the rails on which the telescope turns when it began to move round? A series of safety precautions has been taken to prevent this sort of thing from happening. Before you approach the Big Dish itself, you have to go through a gate in front of the window of the control office. This gate cannot be opened and closed except by means of a switch fitted to the control-room desk, and the controller, as he presses the switch, can see who goes through the gate. Thus, he knows exactly who at any moment is inside the fence surrounding the telescope. No one is unaccounted for. But that is not the end of the safety measures. Everyone inside the telescope fence must be clear of the dish when it begins to tilt. So a second door or, to be more exact, several doors have been fitted inside the telescope

The control room at Jodrell Bank. Dials on the right show the telescope's position in relation to the earth and a universal time clock. Dials on the left show the telescope's position in relation to the Milky Way and a star time clock. (British Information Service)

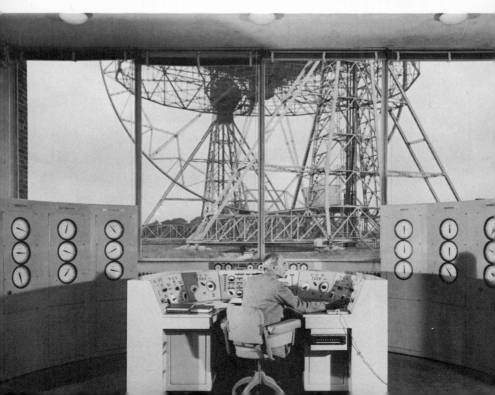

itself. No explorer, scientist, or painter can walk out onto the bowl of the telescope — the part that actually tips — without going through one or other of these doors. Each door has a key in the lock.

Anyone passing through a door unlocks it first, and this action automatically cuts off the current and prevents the dish from being moved. And to show that the door has been deliberately and not accidentally unlocked, anyone going out onto the bowl itself takes the key with him. With the key in his pocket, a man can feel absolutely safe.

To men on the ground, a loud hooter gives warning if the telescope is about to be moved around on its turntable.

There are no houses close to the Big Dish and no railway station, so the people who work there arrive by bus or car. This may sound like an inconvenient arrangement until one remembers it was in order to get away from houses and the electrical disturbance they bring that the telescope was built twenty-five miles south of Manchester and not in the city itself.

The only restaurant at Jodrell Bank is a simple canteen, where everyone, new boy or veteran, eats the same simple meal. The conversation, unlike the cooking, is definitely advanced and spiced with such topics as "total power flux," "band widths," and the like. Next door to the canteen is a lounge, where young graduate students in jeans and shirt sleeves mix with distinguished professors and lecturers.

For afternoon tea, anyone who is on the spot gathers in the entrance hall in front of a small barred window,

rather like the box office at a theater or movie. Tea and
biscuits are handed out through the hatch. The meal is
taken standing.

Wednesday is the day when the people working at
Jodrell Bank see most of each other. At twelve noon they
meet for what is called a colloquium or debate. Here the
professors discuss any new articles, lectures, or research
that has been produced by universities, societies, or scientists anywhere in the world. Sometimes only one item is
dealt with — sometimes several. Then the same day, after
tea, another discussion is held about the progress made at
Jodrell Bank since the previous week.

And now it is time to look more closely at the work.

Many of the graduate students at Jodrell Bank, though
learned in physics or, perhaps, in electrical engineering,
arrive knowing very little about radio astronomy. Let us
suppose for the moment that you are one of them.

2

How a Radio Telescope Works

A radio telescope seems a poor idea at first, since you can't directly see anything with it. Instead, it picks up faint radio waves out of the sky, which, with the help of a sensitive electrical apparatus, can be recorded by a pen making hills and valleys on a moving strip of paper in the same way as a barograph records rises and falls in atmospheric pressure.

If you know the exact part of the sky toward which the radio telescope is pointing, you may be able to pinpoint a radio source. But even if you look at the radio source with an eye telescope, you won't necessarily see anything.

Why, then, are stargazers so enthusiastic about the unseen science of radio astronomy?

The answer is that radio telescopes could help to solve the riddle of the universe in a way that eye telescopes alone cannot manage, no matter how large they may grow.

Astronomy in its time has passed through three different stages, the third of which is the radio telescope, the first of which depended on the naked eye alone.

As far back as 2000 B.C., before even the most primitive water clocks were available, the scientist-researchers, as we should now call them, of Babylon had worked out a system of telling the time by the stars and had divided the day up into hours, minutes, and even seconds. They worked without any form of telescope.

Sailors, too, relied on the stars, when they could see them, to keep their ship on the right course, for until modern times there were no reliable compasses.

Soothsayers and astrologists made a steady income out of predicting future events on earth from what they saw in the heavens.

In other words, the stars and their movements were studied because they were known to be useful and not out of mere curiosity. In the sixteenth century, at just about the time that Henry VIII of England was getting rid of his first wife, a series of fresh discoveries brought new and absorbing interest to the science of astronomy.

A revolutionary book by the Polish astronomer, Nicolaus Copernicus, was published. It revealed for the first time that the earth went around the sun and not the sun around the earth, as people had previously believed. The printed book reached Copernicus only on his deathbed. If he had lived, he might have died under arrest as a heretic, as another astronomer, Galileo, did later. In those days, new ideas that clashed with old ones were treated with suspicion and regarded as dangerous, possibly, to the Christian faith.

Then Tycho Brahe (1546-1601), a former law student, who had shut himself up on a small island not far from the Danish capital of Copenhagen, began to make discoveries. Like many other star trackers, he had taken to astronomy as a hobby. But by the time he was seventeen, he had discovered serious errors in the star tables people then used, and when only twenty-six, he found a new star that is still of interest to radio astronomers. Brahe's observations of the movements of the stars were so accurate that they helped his assistant, Johannes Kepler (1571-1630), to work out the laws governing the movements of the planets. Most of Kepler's work was done before telescopes came into use. It marks the end of chapter one in the history of astronomy.

Chapter two opens with Galileo Galilei (1564-1642), professor of mathematics at the Italian university of Padua. He was not the inventor of the telescope, but he was the first man to make revolutionary discoveries with it. The invention of the telescope is usually credited to Hans Lippershey, a spectaclemaker of Middelburg, Holland, who in 1608 happened to look through two spectacle lenses, held one behind the other at a weathercock, and noticed that it appeared nearer when seen through them. Galileo, however, was the first to apply this newly invented telescope to the field of astronomy.

In the very early 1600's, about the same time as the first British settlers were founding colonies in America, Galileo discovered that the moon was lit with the reflected light of the sun and that the Milky Way consisted of stars rather than luminous haze. He watched the satellites surrounding the planet Jupiter and was the first man to comment on sunspots.

But Galileo's telescope suffered from a big disadvantage. In it, the rays of light coming from the stars passed through a glass lens that "bent" them into focus. White light, however, consists of a mixture of different-colored lights of different wave lengths, from very short-wave violet light at one end of the spectrum, or color range, to long-wave red light at the other end. And each color bends differently, which makes it hard to focus the colors clearly through any one glass. Galileo did not realize why the stars in his telescope were "fuzzy."

Sir Isaac Newton (1642-1727), the man whose studies of gravity are said to have been set off by an apple falling on his head, discovered the reason when he split white light into its various colors by shining it through a glass body. He got around the difficulty by devising a telescope in which the rays of light were concentrated and focused by means of a curved mirror—the system still used today.

In 1755, when Madame de Pompadour still held sway in France at the Court of Louis XV, William Herschel, the son of an orchestra leader, came to England from Germany as oboist in the band of the Hanoverian Guards. Hanover was at that time a British possession.

Later he became an organist and a music teacher at Bath and took up astronomy as a sideline. He believed that Newton's telescope could be improved and, after some two hundred failures, succeeded in casting a mirror for a telescope seven feet long. With this he was able to discover the planet Uranus in 1781, the first new planet found since prehistoric times, and to show that the stars outside our own solar system, which had been thought to be fixed, were moving about the universe at fantastic speeds.

In the 1840's, astronomers first began to calculate the distances between the earth and stars by measuring the apparent changes in the positions of the stars. The probable size and weight of the planets had already been calculated from watching their movements in relation to each other. The next step — still using eye telescopes — was to discover something of the substances making up the sun and other burning stars.

A piece of super detective work was needed here. The evidence was provided by the white light sent out by the sun. As you know, white light is a mixture of lights of different colors. These colors can be separated from one another by passing them through a glass prism, or other suitable device, and can be thrown onto a screen for examination under an instrument known as a spectroscope. Scientists discovered that when sunlight was split up into its various colors, some of the colors that should have been shown on the screen were missing. The missing ones had been soaked up (absorbed, as the scientists say) and lost in the gases surrounding the sun.

Moreover, the scientists were able to show, in laboratory experiments, just what had happened in those blazing gases around the sun. Each gas (oxygen or hydrogen, for example) was absorbing its own particular wave length of light, the exact color depending on the temperature of the gas and various other factors. So the missing colors gave the clue to the chemical make-up of the gases to be found on the surface of the sun.

In 1868, a British scientist, Sir Joseph Lockyer, noticed a big gap in the spectrum or range of light coming from the sun. This missing color — it was in the green section — did not correspond to any of the basic chemical substances then known. But Lockyer was sure that the spectroscope could never lie and was certain that a new and hitherto unknown substance in the area surrounding the sun had absorbed the missing green rays. He named it helium after the Greek name for the sun. Years afterward, the spectroscope was proved right. Helium was found to exist as well in the atmosphere around the earth as a gas that today is used for filling balloons and for many other useful purposes.

Examination of the light from the stars can tell us something about the chemicals to be found there, too, and also give us information about the temperature and pressure on the surface of the stars, the density of the atmosphere, the quality of the light, and even the distance of the various stars from the earth.

But there is still one more thing that the eye telescope tells us about the behavior of the stars, and this is the speed of their movement. To do this, the telescope, or rather the person working it, relies on what is called the Doppler effect.

You get an example of the Doppler effect when an airplane flies past close to you. On the way toward you, the noise of the engines appears to increase and the engine note seems to get more high-pitched. Then, when the plane has passed, the noise of the engine is reduced, as one would expect, and it is also on a lower note.

What has happened is that, when the plane approaches, the sound waves coming from the engine have been apparently shortened and thus become more high-pitched, whereas when the plane is going away from you, the sound waves have been slightly lengthened, that is, lowered in pitch.

Now the Doppler effect works with other waves as well as with sound waves. For instance, if light is sent out from something that is moving toward the observer, the light waves will be shortened, that is, moved away from the red part of the spectrum of light up toward the violet end of the color range. And similarly, if a star is moving away from the observer, the light rays will be lengthened, that is, shifted toward the red end of the spectrum. The amount of the shift varies with the speed of movement.

Meanwhile, the telescopes that now catch the light from the stars and feed it to the spectroscopes had been vastly improved. As you know, a telescope is really a light trap.

If, for example, you have a small three-inch telescope (which means that the glass is three inches across) and you point it at a star, the glass will collect all the light that falls from the star on a circle three inches in diameter.

This is nearly 150 times as much light as you can take from the same star through the pupil of your eye. So even after allowing for some light getting lost inside the telescope, you should be able to see stars that are less than a hundredth of the brightness of the stars you can see with the naked eye.

Obviously, too, you can see much farther into the sky with your telescope than with the naked eye. It is known, for example, that the strength of the light from a given star decreases in proportion to the square of its distance away from the observer. That is, if one star is twice as far away as another star of equal power, the light from the more distant star would be only a quarter as bright. And if the star were three times as far away, the strength of the light would have been reduced by three times three, that is, nine times.

Now we know that, with a three-inch telescope, the observer can see stars a hundred times less bright than those he can see with the naked eye. This means that if the stars give the same quantity and quality of light, the extra distance he can see with his telescope must be the square root of 100 or ten times the distance he could see with the naked eye. But the area of cubic space in the sphere that the observer can see has been increased a great deal more than ten times.

Let's think for a moment of the effect this is going to have. Imagine an observer somewhere on the earth's surface with a clear view all around him. Since he can see an equal distance all around, the limits of his vision are bounded by an imaginary circle. The same holds good if he looks up into the sky. There, too, the boundaries of his vision are circular. In fact, he can see anything in an area the shape of half an orange. The skin of the orange, looked at from inside, represents the limits of his vision. Let us suppose that the orange is four inches across at the widest part, so that the distance from the center to the inside of the skin is two inches. So far, so good. Now suppose that instead of an orange representing the heavens, we had something larger, say a round melon 40 inches across, so that the distance from the center to the inside of the rind was 20 inches. How much bigger would the inside of the melon be than that of the orange? The distance from the center of the melon to the rind is ten times the distance from the center of the orange to its skin. But you'd be wrong if you thought that the inside of the melon was only ten times larger than that of the orange. The answer is ten times ten times ten, the increase in the area of cubic space. And in the same way, if you multiply the distance that the observer can see by ten (which can happen if you give him a telescope), the amount of space he can cover is increased 10 x 10 x 10 times, that is one thousandfold. And if the stars were evenly spaced over the sky, those that could be seen would be multiplied by one thousand as well.

Now just imagine what happens when you increase the diameter of the lens from three inches to two hundred inches, as in the case of the great telescope at Palomar in the San Jacinto Mountains in California. It can pick up stars so remote that the light from them has taken 6,000 million years to reach us. The Mount Palomar telescope relies on a camera rather than the human eye.

In the astronomers' classification, based for historical reasons on the workings of the human eye (and therefore incorrect, actually), each star is given what is called a magnitude to indicate its brightness. A star of the first magnitude is a bright star, and stars with large magnitude numbers are faint. A star with magnitude six is only just visible to the human eye. The light from a star of magnitude five is roughly two and a half times brighter than one of magnitude six. Magnitude four stars are also roughly two and a half times as bright (2.512 times brighter, to be exact) as magnitude five stars, and so on. Thus, it works out that a star of the first magnitude is one hundred times as bright as one of magnitude six. This may seem rather an odd way of classifying the light of stars until you take into account the fact that the human eye works on the same system.

Suppose, for instance, that you were to set out two rows of electric lamps of different strength, some distance away from the observer. Let us also suppose that, in both rows, the lamps are arranged in the order of the strength of light they give, and that in the first row, the lamps increase by the same difference in candle power each time, the first lamp in the row, for example, being 50 watts, the next 100 watts, the next 150 watts, 200 watts, 250 watts, and so on. But in the other row in this experiment, let us suppose that each lamp is twice as strong as the last. Thus,

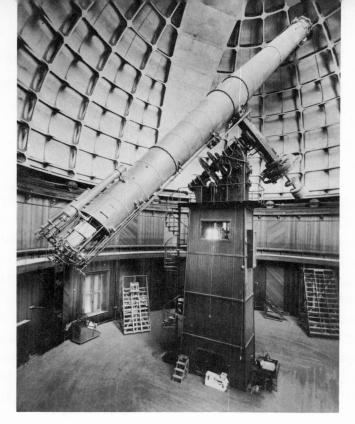

The 36-inch refractor eye telescope at the Lick Observatory, California, showing the equatorial (inclined) mounting. (Lick Observatory Photograph)

the first lamp would, as before, have a 50-watt bulb, and the next 100 watts, but the next would be 200, and the following one 400, and so on.

Now if you were to ask an observer in which of these two rows the lamps were most evenly graduated from dull to bright, the human observer would always choose the second row, in which the light increases by a fixed ratio. This is the way that the human eye happens to work, and so for the convenience of astronomers, the scale of magnitude under which the stars are classified is arranged in the same way.

In practice, however, much of the research carried out by optical telescopes is recorded on film, which is often more reliable than the human eye.

As telescopes improved, they showed the astronomers that they would have to deal with greater and greater distances. For example, the moon is about 240,000 miles from the earth, and light traveling from the moon at about 186,000 miles per second takes about one and a quarter seconds to reach us. The rays of the sun take eight minutes. But the light from Alpha Centauri, the nearest visible star to the earth, takes four and a third years to arrive here. In other words, the star is four and a third light-years away. Alpha Centauri, like the sun, is only one of about ten thousand million stars in the Milky Way galaxy,

Two views of the Milky Way

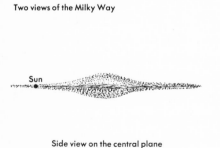

Sun

Side view on the central plane

Sun

View from above

which is so large that light takes 100,000 years to travel from one side of it to the other.

Our own galaxy is shaped something like a poached egg, with the sun — the yolk — rather to one side of the egg. The milky blur that we see at night is really the central part of the galaxy, where the stars are thickest.

At the beginning of the century very little was known about objects outside the galaxy. Their existence had been noted, but they were described as nebulae or clouds. It was not until the 1920's that people began to realize that those clouds were distant galaxies like our own Milky Way. You can see one of them — a smudge of light in the constellation of Andromeda — without a telescope. It is so far away that its light takes the greater part of two million years to reach us. Yet astronomers regard it as being in our own group of galaxies. Other galaxies in other clusters are very much further away. One in Perseus, for example, is 170 million light-years away and one in Cygnus is 550 million light-years. If we take the universe as a whole, there are millions, if not billions, of galaxies.

The farthest distance reached with the largest eye telescope appears currently to be 6,000 million light-years, at which distance photographs have been taken of a galaxy usually known as 3 C 295, in the constellation of Boötes. If a man started traveling toward this point on the day of his birth and continued during all his life, going at the speed of light, and if he lived to be a hundred years old, he would get less than a hundred millionth part of the way there.

The Great Nebula in Andromeda, the nearest spiral galaxy to our own Milky Way. Although two million light-years away, this nebula can be seen with the naked eye. (Mount Wilson and Palomar Observatories)

At very great distances, light waves can tell us little — and the reason, which at first seems strange, is that the more remote galaxies appear to be moving away into outer space. And the more distant they are, the faster they

seem to be moving. For example, the radio source in
Cygnus is receding at about 10,000 miles per second, but
the galaxies in Hydra, farther away, are receding at
37,000 miles per second. Indeed, the speed at which the
more distant galaxies are moving away is so great that the
light waves they send out are "lengthening," as far as we
are concerned, to a point where they will one day no
longer give any light.

Every year, more and more galaxies are nearing the
outer limits at which we can see them, both because the
quantity of light is affected by the increasing distance it
has to come and because the quality of the light is affected
by the Doppler shift toward the dull red end of the spectrum. Many scientists believe that some existing galaxies

*Cygnus "A" radio source, a picture taken with the 200-inch tele-
scope.* (Mount Wilson and Palomar Observatories)

will never be seen by optical telescopes whatever improvements are made.

And this is where radio astronomy takes over.

At such long distances, radio waves sent out by stars and the gases surrounding them are much more powerful than the corresponding light waves. This is the case particularly when galaxies collide with one another. One other thing enters into the enthusiasm of astronomers for the radio telescope — the fact that it is virtually unaffected by fog, smog, or cloud, which prevent light waves from reaching an eye telescope.

The radio waves on which radio telescopes depend are often compared to ripples on a pond, and although this comparison is not entirely accurate, it is a useful one. If you drop a stone into a calm pond, the effect is to send a series of ripples or small waves across the water. And if you were quick enough, you could measure the distance between the crest of one of these waves and the next. If the waves were evenly spaced, this would give you what could be called a wave length.

And if, in addition, you timed the ripples as they reached the edge of the pond, this would give you the frequency of the waves per second or per minute as the case might be.

Radio waves also have a wave length and a frequency, and since they travel at a constant speed, there is a definite relationship between the wave length and the frequency. Thus, if a radio wave has a length of one meter, the "ripples" reach the receiver at a frequency of about

300,000,000 waves per second. Whereas, if the wave is twice as long, it will have only half that number of waves or cycles per second. In other words, it has a lower frequency.

When a radio wave, passing through the air, reaches an aerial connected to a suitably placed receiving circuit, it sets up a similar electric impulse in the circuit. But this doesn't take us very far because when an ordinary well-behaved electric impulse or current travels along a wire, there is no outward and visible effect. You have to imagine what goes on inside the wire. The metal along which the current passes consists of millions of atoms. Each atom consists of a nucleus or center surrounded by a number of particles known as electrons. These electrons can move freely along the wire, and this is what happens when an electric current is passed through the wire. The electrons move along the wire at the same speed as the radio wave that has sent them on their journey, and when the impulse ceases, they return to their former position around a nucleus. Consequently, when radio waves reach a receiver, the electrons in the receiving circuit are in a constant ebb and flow from one end of the circuit to the other, moving first in one direction and then in the opposite direction, back to where they started from.

The length of the receiving circuit must be exactly right in order to get good reception, for if it is too long or too short, the electrons that have to flow to and from the end of the circuit will be out of step with the timing of the radio waves. This is the reason a radio set has to be tuned in in order to receive any station clearly. The tuning has the effect of lengthening or shortening the receiving circuit, so that the set resonates or echoes properly to the wave length that its owner wants it to receive.

Karl Jansky, a young American engineer, was the first man in the world to listen seriously to the radio waves sent out by the stars in outer space. While still an undergraduate at the University of Wisconsin, he was found to be suffering from an incurable kidney disease and was ordered by his doctor to lead a quiet life. He took a position with the Bell Telephone Laboratories in 1928 and was given the job of tracking down atmospherics and other noises likely to interfere with long-distance commercial radio-telephone work. His "laboratory" was a former potato farm at Holmdel, New Jersey.

For his research he used a long 100-foot aerial mounted on a pair of ancient motorcar wheels that permitted it to be moved around horizontally in any direction. By changing the position of the aerial, Jansky found that he could trace the sources of most of the interference.

There was one noise that baffled him. It was a faint but steady hissing noise. It was not the kind of interference that came from a power station or from another radio transmitter because its direction moved throughout each day. At first, since the source seemed to move from east to west, Jansky thought that the hiss might perhaps be caused by the sun. But after a time the faint sizzling sound got right out of step with the sun. Eventually Jansky found that the strongest "hiss" came when the aerial was aimed at a definite part of the sky — namely at the position of the Milky Way.

In December, 1932, Jansky published a paper in the

journal, *Proceedings of the Institute of Radio Engineers,* describing the radio signals that he was receiving from the Milky Way. That paper marked the true birthday of radio astronomy.

Jansky's report appeared in both popular newspapers and in scientific journals, and a New York radio station relayed his "message from the stars." But the world remained, for the most part, unruffled.

Most radio men were not directly interested in astronomy, and few astronomers wanted to bother with radio. Jansky tried to persuade his employers to take up radio "space research." But they said no. For a while Jansky tried to carry on his experiments on his own time, but his health failed. He died in 1950 with his dreams unfulfilled.

One fellow-countryman, Grote Reber, grasped the importance of Jansky's work and built himself a radio telescope. Reber was an amateur who carried out his experiments for fun and paid for them himself. He set up his telescope in his own back yard at Wheaton, Illinois. It worked on the same principle as a bowl-type electric heater. But whereas the bowl of an electric heater reflects the heat outward from the center of the bowl into the room, the telescope worked in reverse. The bowl caught the radio waves from the sky and reflected them onto Reber's receiving circuit in the center of the bowl of his telescope.

Reber's radio telescope, built in 1937, was the first in the world and was the forerunner of the "Big Dish." It was thirty feet across — not large by present day-standards — but Reber found that by using sensitive receivers, he could work on a much shorter wave length than the one that Jansky had used (60 centimeters instead of 15 meters), which in turn made more accurate observations possible. Reber was able to make sky maps that showed clearly that the radio sky was quite different from the visible one. Some of the brightest stars gave out no radio waves to speak of, whereas strong radio impulses came from dark areas of sky in which there had been no reason to suspect activity. From 1940 onwards, Reber's papers began to attract the attention of serious astronomers.

During World War II, radio men and astronomers both became interested in the science of radar, the invention that made it possible to spot enemy planes or ships in darkness or fog by bouncing radio waves off them. From the direction of the "bounce" and the time required for it to return, the men in charge of a scanner could tell the distance and direction of a hostile plane or vessel. At the same time, the enemy did everything possible to prevent their opponents' radar from working properly, and radar experts had to spend a great deal of time trying to determine how much of the interference they met with was due to the enemy and how much to natural causes. But, unlike Jansky and Reber, they had official help.

In Britain they found that radio waves came both from meteor trails and from spots on the sun, and from then on people began to study the radio sky for its own sake. The alliance between the radio experts and the astronomers was complete.

No radio telescope on the earth's surface, however

sensitive, can pick up all radio waves from the stars. The reason is that the earth has around it a layer of electrified air called the ionosphere, extending upward from about a hundred miles above the surface to about double that distance. (The thickness depends partly on the amount of sunlight received.) If it were not for the ionosphere, radio waves from broadcasting stations would never be able to travel long distances around the world but would continue straight out into space and be lost. Instead, the ionosphere prevents the shorter radio waves from escaping, and they continue bouncing between the surface of the earth and

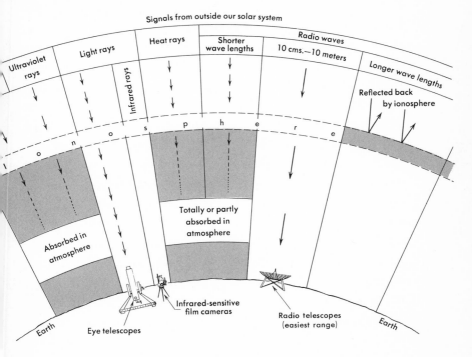

the shell of the ionosphere and so stay within the range of our radio receivers. But, in the same way that the shell of the ionosphere prevents most radio impulses from leaving the earth's atmosphere, so it keeps some other radio waves from reaching the earth from outer space. Wave lengths of over 10 meters in length are reflected back into space by the ionosphere, and those below 1 centimeter, though they pass through the ionosphere, tend to be absorbed in the earth's atmosphere. This leaves only the range between 10 meters and 1 centimeter for radio-telescope work, and in practice few radio telescopes can cope with wave lengths much below 10 centimeters. And this is not the end of the difficulty. The wave lengths of these radio impulses are millions of times longer than those of light. Consequently, the apparatus that focuses them has to be much larger, too. For example, the 200-inch eye telescope at Mount Palomar can focus light far more accurately than the 250-foot apparatus at Jodrell Bank can focus radio waves.

The readings of most radio telescopes cover a fairly wide area of sky at the wave lengths they are able to receive. Thus, when the radio telescope is pointing in a certain direction, it receives the whole of the radiation coming from that area of the sky. Under these conditions, one large radio star may outdazzle all its neighbors, or perhaps several small stars may appear as one large one.

These are only two of the problems with which the pioneers of radio astronomy have had to contend. Let us see what they have managed to discover.

3

What a Radio Telescope "Sees"

The light from the sun is so dazzling that it blots out the stars in the sky by day. But the radio waves from the sun, although relatively strong, don't dazzle radio telescopes. Therefore, radio telescopes can pick up signals from the stars outside the galaxy by day as well as by night. The "radio" sun is, however, both wasteful and undependable as a radio beacon. It is wasteful because no transmitter needs to be as hot as the sun is in order to send out radio waves. It is undependable because the sun has at least two entirely different radio moods. Radio experts, for example, distinguish between what they call the "quiet sun" and the "active sun." When the sun is quiet, there is no unexpected radio activity. But when the sun is active, it can distort the radio atmosphere to such an extent that is is impossible to receive properly.

The radio storms of the active sun are connected with sunspots and with sun flares.

A sunspot is a dark area on the sun's surface that can occasionally be seen with the naked eye when the sun is covered by a thin veil of cloud. (If you value your eyesight, don't look at the sun directly but only through properly smoked glass, which, in the case of a telescope, should be designed for use with that instrument.) A sunspot is cooler than the rest of the sun and gives out less heat, but on the other hand, it is magnetically more active and can send out radio signals on the one-meter band for several days at a time. Sunspots are sometimes half as big as the United States and may remain visible after a complete revolution of the sun, which takes the best part of four weeks. Other radio disturbances occur in areas of the sun known as calcium plages, which are local heat spots, also with strong magnetic fields. Radiation from these plages can last for several weeks.

The solar flares, which can be seen projecting at times from the outer rim of the sun, can also lead to very strong outbursts of radio activity. Almost immediately after a flare has been seen, a powerful invasion of X-rays (the kind that are used to photograph bones in human beings) arrives here. This volley of X-rays disturbs the ionosphere in just the same way as a pebble dropped into a pond disturbs the reflections on the surface. And because the ionosphere has been roughed up, our own radio communications are upset. Radio signals, instead of glancing smoothly off the lower side of the ionosphere, bounce off at impossible angles. Then, after a few minutes or even seconds, the disturbance dies down, in the same way as the flare.

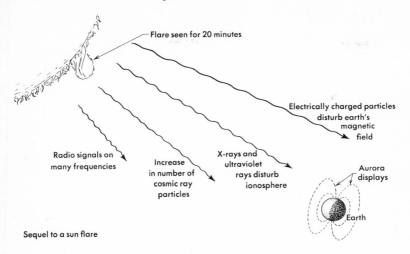

Flare seen for 20 minutes

Electrically charged particles
disturb earth's
magnetic
field

Radio signals on
many frequencies

Increase
in number of
cosmic ray
particles

X-rays and
ultraviolet
rays disturb
ionosphere

Aurora
displays

Earth

Sequel to a sun flare

Meantime, the flare has also set off a wave of particles, known as cosmic rays. The particles travel away from the sun and pass through the various layers of the sun's atmosphere or corona, as it is called, stirring up each layer in turn, from the densest ones nearest to the sun, to the most rarified layers nearer to the earth.

After the electrical particles have passed through the various layers of the corona, they (or some of them) then make for the earth. They travel comparatively slowly at a speed of about 1,000 miles per second, and instead of reaching the earth in eight minutes as light from the sun would, they take somewhat over a day. When they arrive, they upset the ionosphere all over again and for a much longer period. There is often radio chaos. A short-wave broadcast that is meant to be local to Paris is picked up in Miami or Teheran. Medium-wave transmission gets

lost somewhere up in the "ceiling." Eventually the particles come within the earth's magnetic field. (The earth is
a magnet, and like any other magnet has two "poles" or
points of attraction at opposite ends to each other.)

The striking spectacles known as Northern Lights in
the Northern Hemisphere and Southern Lights in the
Southern Hemisphere are due to streams of electrical particles being drawn toward the earth's magnetic poles.
Neither of the magnetic poles is in the same position as
the geographic North and South Poles. It follows that in
their efforts to reach a magnetic pole, the particles will
swerve all over the place, and instead of the storm affect-
ing only the sunny side of the earth, as the X-ray burst
did, a wide range of places will be bombarded by the
invaders.

This seems a logical explanation of what happens when
the sun flares up, although a lot of careful research on
different types of flare has still to be carried out.

Another mystery that radio telescopes are helping to
solve concerns the great difference in the temperatures
that surround the sun. The heat at the center of the sun is
produced by a process something like the one inside a
nuclear bomb. Burning hydrogen is being changed into
helium at the rate of 500 tons per second at a temperature
in the neighborhood of 20 million degrees Centigrade.
But at the edge of the sun the temperature is only 6,000
degrees Centigrade. (Scientists can measure the temperature of the sun by splitting up sunlight and analyzing its
quality.)

The most astonishing thing is that the temperature of the sun's corona, that is, the atmosphere surrounding the sun, is many times higher than that of the sun itself.

It is hard to explain how the electric particles sent out by the sun get the speed and power to travel 93,000,000 miles to the earth. Physicists in many different countries use machines to speed up the movement of electrical particles by forcing them to follow a curved path, and they think the action that takes place in and around the sun may be similar to what goes on inside the machines.

One of the interesting discoveries made by the radio telescope is that the sun's corona extends very much farther than was formerly believed. Eye telescopes cannot help much here, as the corona is transparent in much the same way as the part of the flame nearest to a match head. But radio telescopes can detect radio activity even in thin air.

An unusual technique is used for this purpose, which was discovered at an early stage in the story of radio astronomy. The radio pioneers said to themselves, "Famous astronomers travel thousands of miles in order to *see* an eclipse. We, too, should be able to learn something from eclipses, not the ones that can be seen, but radio eclipses." So they waited for the moment when the sun would come between the earth and a radio star, thus eclipsing the radio source. This event happens every year in the middle of June when the sun passes close to the Crab nebula, which lies between the horns of the Taurus or Bull constellation.

In 1952, radio astronomers at Cambridge succeeded in watching the effects. They found that the radio waves coming from the Crab were bent by the corona of the sun in the same way as water bends or refracts the image of a stick plunged into it. This refraction, however, took place even when the sun itself was not in the way of the radio star. Measurements showed that the corona, which caused the refraction, extended very much farther from the sun than had previously been thought, and indeed it is almost possible that the earth itself is on the fringe of the sun's corona, though at this distance the corona is probably very thin and rarified if it exists at all.

So much for the sun. What have the radio astronomers discovered about the moon?

In the first place, radio astronomers have been able to confirm what had already been suspected, that there is almost no atmosphere on the moon. But there is *some.* To prove this, the radio men repeated their experiment of a radio eclipse, with the same star — the Crab nebula — that they'd used for the sun. As the moon passed in front of the Crab, radio signals coming from the Crab should have been cut off for 59 minutes, 12 seconds, whereas, in fact, there was a cutoff lasting for 59 minutes, 36 seconds, or twelve seconds longer at each side of the moon. This was not very much, but it was long enough to show some kind of obstruction, in other words, atmosphere. The moon's atmosphere, however, is far too thin to support any of the forms of life that we know. A man who reaches the moon will be living, for all practical purposes, in a vacuum.

It has not yet been possible to find out what the moon is made of because, unlike the sun, it is not in flames and therefore gives out no light of its own that could be analyzed to see what substances are being burned. However, the moon does have a temperature of a sort.

How is this temperature measured? It would, of course, be no good to point a thermometer at the moon because any ordinary heat waves would have been completely absorbed in the atmosphere long before they reached the earth. But when anything is hot to the touch, it follows that other activity is present, too. There are waves akin to heat waves but with a shorter wave length, known as infrared rays. The wave length of these infrared rays is just too long for us to see with the human eye, but they can be picked up on photographic film or plate, and these photographs allow the infrared temperature to be measured. Similarly, the waves at the other end — the long-wave end of the range of heat waves — are not so very different from the shortest radio waves that can be picked up by radio astronomers.

New and very sensitive apparatus has been designed within the last few years for picking up these very short radio waves. Indeed, a comparatively small radio telescope can now in theory pick up radio waves produced by the temperature changes in an iceberg one thousand miles away. One of these inventions is the maser (the initials stand for Microwave Amplification by the Stimulated Emission of Radiation). The maser is really an apparatus that can store up radio waves pumped into it and send them out on a given wave length when it is stimulated by a radio wave of the same length.

The radio activity of the moon has been measured during each of the 29½ days that the moon takes to go around the earth, and the results show that the moon is an extremely cold place. One interesting fact is that the temperature varies by about 30 degrees during the lunar month. The reason is that, at full moon, the moon gets the full rays of the sun, whereas, at the new moon, the moon is cut off from the sun by the earth. But the moon's temperature does not really begin to rise until four days after the sun reaches it. This fact suggests that the outside of the moon carries a layer of dust, which slows up changes of temperature, acting in the same way as insulating material placed in roofs or attics or the wrapping that we put around hot pipes. In fact, the temperature chart of the moon seems to show that a large part of its surface is covered by dust or sand, which would form an excellent blanket especially if there were no air between the grains.

It is now almost twenty years since the first radio waves were sent out from the earth to the moon and caught again on the rebound. A Hungarian scientist named Zoltan Bay was first in the field. He realized that the moon's echo was likely to be extremely faint, but he calculated it should arrive back — if it did — in two and a half seconds. Then he analyzed the signals received on his set at exactly two and a half seconds after his own signal went out and found that there really was an echo. Since then, bouncing radio waves off the moon has been done repeatedly, and in May, 1959, the Big Dish at Jodrell Bank succeeded in aiming a radio message to the moon that bounced off and was duly received in the U.S. Later a teleprinter message was sent in the same way to Australia. At Jodrell Bank they also have a tape recording of part of Brahms' Fourth Symphony that was bounced off the moon. Listening to the tape, you hear first a bar or two of the symphony broadcast from Jodrell Bank and a couple of seconds later the same sounds echoing back from the moon.

One day perhaps the moon will act as the site for a relay broadcasting station. The plan would be to send the relay station to the moon by rocket and deposit it there. The batteries for the receiver and transmitter would be maintained with energy supplied by the sun. The relay station would, of course, be reached by transmissions on short waves, which would pass through the ionosphere both coming and going. These waves would not be disrupted by such things as sunspots and flares, which throw ordinary radio transmissions out of gear. This is the first advantage to be gained by keeping in radio touch with the moon. The second possibility is that, by sending radio waves to and fro, we may learn a thing or two about conditions far above the earth.

The moon could also be used as a reference point for

a radio sextant for navigators. At present, seamen who want to find their position do so either by "dead reckoning" (that is by calculating the distance and the courses they have sailed from their starting point) or by taking sights with an eye sextant of the position of the sun, moon, or stars at a recorded moment of time. But dead reckoning can go wrong if there are unsuspected currents or compass faults, and no one can take sights if the sky is covered with cloud. With a radio sextant, life for the navigator might be a good deal simpler. When a radio wave is bounced off the moon, it is already possible to tell from the time taken to go there and back which area of the moon it has hit, and, in time, still more accurate radio sights can be expected.

Meanwhile, let us see what the radio telescope can tell us about two of the planets.

First take Venus, the planet 26 million miles away from the earth, which the Russians first aimed for in February, 1961. Venus has been a tantalizing planet because she is hidden from the earth by a layer of thick cloud. The only light coming from Venus is what is reflected from the sun by these clouds. Scientists, however, have been able to form some ideas about the atmosphere beneath the cloud. They do so by comparing the sunlight reaching the earth directly with the light reflected to the earth by the Venus cloud barrier. The difference between the two shows the effect of Venus's atmosphere on the light. From these experiments it is pretty certain that the traveler to Venus would have to take his own oxygen mask with him if he wanted to survive. Most of the atmosphere appears to consist of carbon dioxide, the gas that puts life into fizzy drinks but not into animals.

Temperature measurements of the surface of Venus brought one interesting fact to light, almost by accident. Venus takes only 225 days to go around the sun as compared with our own 365 days. So it follows that at one season of the year Venus and the earth are on the same side of the sun, whereas, later, they will be on opposite sides. The best radio contacts occur naturally when Venus is nearest the earth. At this point the sun is shining on the far side of Venus, and "our" side is in the shade. Radio astronomers expected that Venus's temperature in the shade might be low. But surprisingly enough the readings were high. So the question is this: "Is there some special reason why the shady side of Venus manages to retain the heat of the sun, or is it merely that the planet is revolving so quickly that its whole surface is kept warm?" At the time this is being written no one has discovered the answer.

After Venus, the next most interesting planet is Jupiter. Jupiter's radio signals were discovered also by accident by two U.S. scientists, Dr. Bernard Burke and Dr. Kenneth Franklin, of the Carnegie Institution in Washington, when they left an experimental aerial designed to receive at a fairly long wave length pointing at the sun's path for two months in succession. The records showed some very strong signals coming from varying spots in the sky at different times of day. And the only source that could have caused them was Jupiter. At first Jupiter's strong signals were believed to have been set off by thunderstorms, but closer examination showed that they were more likely to be the result of sunspot activity on the planet. The strange thing, however, is that they come only from one part of Jupiter, near, but not in, a feature called the Great Red Spot. The way in which the position of the radio source was discovered is interesting. Observers through optical telescope have known for years that Jupiter's day lasts a little under ten hours. But the part of Jupiter lying at the equator revolves more quickly than the parts at the poles, due to Jupiter's molten state, and takes about five minutes less to make a complete revolution. Hence, by seeing exactly how long the radio source takes to make a complete turn, radio astronomers could work out how near the poles the radio source was and how near the equator.

Another field in which radio astronomers have done well is that of meteors.

Meteors are small particles, usually of iron, nickel, or stone, which enter the earth's atmosphere about 70 miles overhead and burn up when they do so because of friction. They eventually settle as dust on the earth. Those meteors that are too large to burn up and that land on the earth's surface are called meteorites.

The average observer can pick out about six meteors an hour on a reasonably quiet night, but radio astronomers have figures running up to two hundred a minute, and one of them has calculated that ten tons is added to the earth's weight every day from this bombardment.

At certain times of the year, meteors appear in what are called showers, and it has been established that these showers are the remains of former comets — miniature flaming worlds that buzz around the sun, some once every three or four years, some once in a hundred or even a thousand years.

The comet and the sun are rather like the moth and the candle. Often the sun ends by burning up the comet. The radiation from the sun in the very thin atmosphere in which the comet moves is enough to "blow" or move the tail of the comet so that it always points away from the sun. One astronomer actually watched a comet breaking up. He saw it first as a whole comet, and then, when it returned to view six and a half years later, he noticed that it had split into two parts. After another six and a half years, these two parts were separated from one another by more than a million miles. Since then, whenever the earth has crossed the comet's path, there have been spectacular showers of meteors. This, then, is the connection between comets and showers of meteors. For example, the Perseids, to be seen each year around August 12, were once part of Tuttle's Comet, and the Leonids in November came from Temple's Comet.

Apart from the groups of meteors following in the path of a comet, there are the "free lance" or, if you prefer it, "lone star" meteors that appear to have no relation with each other. All go in different directions and without warning.

It is a curious fact, however, that more sporadic meteors will be seen after midnight than before, because from midnight on, the observer will be in front of the earth in its path around the sun and can therefore see those meteors coming to meet the earth as well as those overtaking it. For centuries these meteors had fascinated astronomers, for even when meteors could be seen overtaking the earth, they arrived too quickly and too unexpectedly for plotting with eye telescopes. No one, therefore, knew whether they had always traveled within our solar system or whether they had come from outer space. This mystery has now been solved by radio telescopes. As far back as 1945, two British astronomers, Stanley Hey and Gordon S. Stewart, who were studying radar interference, discovered that the head and the tail of a meteor give a radar echo when the meteor crosses the radar beam at right angles. And what is more, they were able to pick up meteors during the day, which had never previously been possible. Later, remarkable progress was made by Professor Lovell at Jodrell Bank, and it was found possible to work out the speed of the meteors entering the earth's atmosphere. They were not traveling fast enough for their course to be independent of the solar system. Therefore, they did not come from outer space.

Anything that is a strong radio source, whether it is showy or not, interests radio astronomers. For example, the Crab nebula in the constellation of Taurus remains a big attraction, although it was still more interesting 900 years ago when the Chinese first noticed what they thought was a new star. In actual fact, it was an immense blowout by an old star, which, until then, had been burning steadily like our own sun. The blowout actually happened 4,000 years earlier than the Chinese saw it because the earth is 4,000 light-years from the Crab. It came when the star overheated and began to behave just like a hydrogen bomb exploding, with atoms fusing together to form new elements.

Eventually the heat became so terrific that the whole of the center of the star blew itself to pieces. And in the meantime, the star's light had increased until it was many million times stronger than the sun's. Today the Crab nebula can still be seen aglow more than 900 years after

The Crab nebula, a supernova, the explosion of which was noticed by the Chinese in 1054 A.D.; *it is still a radio source. Picture was taken in red light.* (Mount Wilson and Palomar Observatories)

the big bang became visible. But very little of its original body remains, and what there is takes the form of cloud and dust.

A star that erupts and throws off a piece of itself and flares up during the process is called a nova because to the unsuspecting it appears as a new star. But a whole star that explodes, as the Crab did, has a far more brilliant light than a nova and is called a supernova.

Radio astronomers have discovered several other remains of supernova stars. The one noticed by Tycho Brahe in 1572 and another by Kepler in 1604 are still traceable by radio telescopes, and there is also Cassiopeia, one of the brightest radio sources in the sky. Cassiopeia began to blow up about 260 years ago, but no one noticed it at the time.

Another concealed "radio station" exists in the constellation of Cygnus the Swan. This radio source was first noticed by Stanley Hey in 1946. But, when Graham Smith of Cambridge, England, another well-known radio astronomer, tried to pinpoint the position, he could find no star that could account for the signals. So the Cambridge group sent particulars of the position of their radio source to the team operating the giant 200-inch eye telescope at Mount Palomar, and the telescope was trained on the spot and pictures were taken. The results were amazing. The photographs showed an object shaped something like a dumbell, now believed to be two galaxies in collision at a distance of 550 million light-years away.

A photograph believed to be that of two galaxies in collision taken on the 200-inch telescope at Mount Palomar. The object appears to be a radio source. (Mount Wilson and Palomar Observatories)

Here the word "collision" does not mean that the stars in the two galaxies concerned actually hit each other. They are believed to be too widely spaced for that. But the gases that surround the stars in the galaxies are under pressure and in a state of agitation, which causes them to give out powerful radio waves.

Now the fact that these two galaxies were easily found and resolved at distances beyond the range of all but the largest eye telescopes suggests that as improvements are made to radio telescopes, they will gradually outdistance the eye telescope in the race to find out what is happening in the remote reaches of outer space. In fact, the Cygnus source would be detectable today by a radio telescope even if it were ten times as far away as it is.

One of the most exciting radio discoveries concerns the shape of our own galaxy. We have quite a lot of information and photographs about the other galaxies and know that some of them are circular, some oval, some spiral, and some irregular. But until recently we knew little or nothing about our own galaxy. And because of the dust and debris of the Milky Way, it is impossible to discover much with an ordinary eye telescope, no matter how powerful. If it were not for this dust, the light from the stars would be strong enough to give us perpetual daylight around the clock. Nevertheless, it is possible to see with eye telescopes that the galaxy is rotating and that the stars in the center are moving faster than those at the outside. But only a radio telescope could make a proper survey. A Dutch scientist, Hendrik van de Hulst of Leyden, Holland, working at a time when his country was occupied by the Germans during World War II, made this possible. He found that hydrogen exists in the atmosphere in two slightly different states, distinguished from each other by the position occupied by the single electron belonging to each hydrogen atom.

The hydrogen gas surrounding the stars in the Milky Way is very rarified, but there are enough atoms in it for collisions to occur, altering the position of the electron and changing the hydrogen from one form to the other. Then, a minute radio impulse or "ping" is sent out, and experiments in the laboratory have shown that this "ping" is on a wave length of 21 centimeters.

The wave length, shown by the number of pulses per second, can be measured exactly — so accurately, in fact, that if the cloud from which the "ping" has come is on the move, this fact can be detected from the slight variations in the pulsation count produced in accordance with the Doppler theory.

The result is that when a radio telescope is pointed at any chosen part of the galaxy, it will record the speeds at which the hydrogen clouds in that part are moving apparently toward or away from the observer. And since we already know the speed at which the stars and clouds at different distances from the center of the galaxy should be moving, we can work out how near to the center of the galaxy each radio cloud is. All the information has to be adjusted, of course, to cut out differences in readings due to the earth's changing position, and the sun is used as the basic point of reference. Without mathematics, it is impossible to get anywhere in radio astronomy.

4

Why They Built the Big Dish

The radio telescope shaped like an electric heater, with a single adjustable aerial, is only one of many different types of radio telescopes built with different purposes in mind. Some work only at, or close to, a particular wave length. Others, instead of a single aerial, have many. And in order to understand just where the Big Dish fits into the picture, it is necessary to know a little about some of these types. What does the Big Dish do that the others can't?

Naturally, the first problem with any radio telescope is to fit in an aerial large enough to pick up the very faint radiations that come from distant galaxies or hydrogen clouds. The bigger the aerial, the stronger the radiation that can be picked up from a single source. But large aerials are costly to build and need expensive sites, and if too much wiring has to be used — some take forty miles of wire — to carry the radiation to the instrument that records it, some of the gain is lost.

Making a big enough aerial is not the only difficulty. Another problem with radio telescopes is to distinguish one radio source in the sky from another. The radio astronomers like to be sure of receiving one star at a time and not two — one perhaps millions of miles nearer than the other. The difficulty of distinguishing one radio star from another close to it (or "resolving" stars as the scientists say) arises from the fact that radio wave lengths are long in comparison with those of light.

For example, the wave length of the light coming from a star is measured in millionths of a centimeter, whereas radio waves run in centimeters if not meters. It then follows that a radio wave is more easily distorted by the receiving apparatus than a light wave. And longer radio waves are more seriously distorted than short waves. If you were thinking of making two radio telescopes equally accurate, one to work on a ten-centimeter wave length and the other to receive on ten meters, the latter telescope would need to be one hundred times the size of the other; and it has been calculated that a radio telescope, in order to get the same power of resolution possessed by a moderate-sized eye telescope, would need an aerial several thousand miles long.

Radio astronomers have found one way around the difficulty of improving resolution by using what is called an "interferometer." A radio "interferometer" is really a very clever idea borrowed by radio astronomers from other scientists who use interferometers for the study of light. Literally, an interferometer is something that interferes

Part of the Mullard Observatory interferometer at Cambridge, England. This nonmobile but tiltable aerial stretches in an east-west direction for nearly 500 yards. (Keystone)

with light or radio waves so as to rearrange their pattern. Anyone can make a very simple form of light interferometer for himself. For example, if a card, pierced with two identical very small pinholes, is placed in front of a single source of light, some of the rays passing through the pinholes will spread outward, having been interfered with by the edges of the pinholes.

If these spread-out rays are thrown onto a screen, they will be seen to form a series of lines because the light rays from the pinholes have varying distances to go before reaching the screen. You can imagine some of them getting there on the crest of the wave, while others arrive half a wave length later. When two waves, one from each pinhole, arrive in tune, the amount of light shown on the screen is greater than when they arrive out of tune. Now two radio aerials joined together with one receiver can act in the same way as the pinholes. If a source is exactly the same distance from each of them, the radio waves will arrive at exactly the same time. But if the two aerials are continually altering their distance from the source, which happens when a star "moves across the sky" because of the rotation of the earth, then the waves will arrive at the receiving end sometimes in tune and sometimes out of tune.

When the waves are in tune or "in phase," as the radio men say, the impulse received by the aerials is increased. But when the waves are out of tune, the impulses from the two aerials counteract each other, and cancel out the effect on the receiver.

A radio telescope (interferometer type) detects a radio source

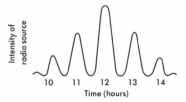

(a) Pattern produced by wide-angle source
with aerials close together

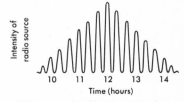

(b) Pattern produced by narrower-angle
source with aerials farther apart

Thus, if you were keeping a pen and ink record of the radio impulses received from a star passing over the two aerials of an interferometer, you would get a series of peaks in the graph as the star passed positions where the radio waves were in phase and a corresponding number of valleys where the waves were out of phase. ("Fringe pattern" is the proper term to describe this wavy record.)

The fringe pattern of ups and downs can be made finer and sharper by moving the two aerials farther apart so that it resembles a pine forest rather than a series of gentle molehills.

At this point, you may well ask how this helps the radio astronomer to get better resolution and thus to sort out one small star from another. The answer is that, if the right distances are used, only radio stars of small diameter can produce a fringe pattern, since with a source as big, for example, as the sun, one edge of the source would be out of phase when the other would be in phase, and no proper pattern would be formed unless the position of the receivers was altered.

And the farther apart the aerials are placed, the more "choosy" they become and the more inclined they are to reject the bigger radio stars and sources. In fact, it is possible to measure the diameter of radio stars by seeing how far apart the aerials have to be moved before the pattern breaks up. Of course, radio interferometers can have many more than two aerials. At least one of them has 64 aerials connected to one receiver.

Radio telescopes have been improved in a number of

other ways. For example, the receiving apparatus can be designed to record only the *changes* in radiation and to cut out the background noise such as you get, for example, from the Milky Way.

And the action of an interferometer can be speeded up, too. Normally, as we have seen, the fringe pattern recorded by a radio interferometer is built up because the earth's rotation causes the waves from a single source to arrive periodically in phase and out of phase at the aerials being used. But the changes due to the earth's rotation are comparatively slow, and normally each peak in the fringe pattern is separated by several minutes from the next, which means that the normal type of interferometer would be of little use in recording events such as sun flares, which sometimes last only for a very short time.

This handicap was overcome by artificially increasing the speed with which the fringe pattern is formed, without altering the position of the aerials. This can be done by introducing an automatic switch that regularly alters the relationship between the two aerials so that the graph record rises to a peak at a point where the waves are exactly out of phase as well as when they are exactly in phase.

Another radio telescope that makes use of this "circuit-changing" technique is the Mills Cross type, which consists of two longish aerials arranged in the form of a cross. By changing the circuit of the current rapidly, the sensitive spot at the point where the two aerials intersect can be turned into the real eye of this form of telescope.

When an interferometer in the form of a cross or two

arms at right angles to each other is being used, the aerials of the east-west arm are usually fixed and those of the north-south arm are movable to allow the telescope to be used for stars of higher or lower elevation. To alter the wave length of the receiver may, however, be a complicated process, and miles of rewiring may be necessary.

One way of reducing the cost of a radio telescope is to build up the information that would be received by one large-sized radio receiver by taking readings with small or less expensive aerials and by assembling a composite paste-and-scissors picture from them by what is called the "unfilled aperture" technique. But only a computing machine can handle the thousands of calculations this method involves, and the build-up process is very slow.

All fixed telescopes, including the Mills Cross, suffer from one serious disadvantage. With at least one of their aerials pegged, they can scan only a relatively small strip of sky. And like a person with a stiff neck lying on his back, they can take in only one portion of that strip of sky as it comes overhead. In practice, it is not enough to be able to pick up a radio star at only one period of the day — when it passes over the same longitude as the observer. One should be able to follow it around, and, in addition, the receiving aerial must be big. This has been the whole idea behind the Big Dish.

The man who fought for the existence of the Big Dish and who persuaded the world that it was really worth having a giant radio telescope is Professor Sir Bernard Lovell, known to all at Jodrell Bank as "the Prof." He comes

from Bristol, the home of Cabot, the explorer who reached
the mainland of America some years ahead of Christopher
Columbus. But Lovell, the most modern of explorers, has
his roots right in the Cheshire village where he lives. For
example, he likes cricket and is captain of the local village
team. He is fond of gardening — particularly shrubs, of
which he has nearly five hundred. He is musical and, like
Herschel, took to playing the organ. He likes Bach — but
also the familiar hymns at the village church.

Success has not changed Lovell or taken his eye off
the radio sky. Even when he is supposed to be on holiday,
he can't resist coming to work for an hour or two.

His attitudes are nonchalant, and he will often lean
against the nearest door or window when thinking hard.
But one does not have to be with him long before realiz-
ing that he is as much a man of action as a thinker. His
eyes are bright blue, with a penetrating quality. His nose
is sharp and inquiring. His voice is deep, with the slightest
trace of a West Country rasp and with far more authority
than you would expect in a lecture room. His frame is
athletic; his hands are restless.

Some people meeting him for the first time might think
him a little shy and even aloof. This impression may be
due to the fact that "the Prof," when talking, is apt (except
on radio or TV, when he is excellent) to think about three
sentences ahead of what he is actually saying.

Unlike many explorers, he became famous and successful comparatively early in life. He first came to Manchester University as Assistant Lecturer in Physics at the

age of twenty-three and at once began research into the showers of atomic particles that cause the Aurora Borealis or Northern Lights. In 1939, at the outbreak of World War II, Lovell was snapped up by defense experts who were interested in radar.

After the war, Lovell came back to Manchester University as a full-fledged lecturer, but his wartime experiences had only made him keener to find out more about the cosmic rays and other "blips" and queer traces that had been appearing on his radar instruments without any good reason to account for them. But it was impossible to work at Manchester itself because of the interference from cars, radio sets, and many other electric appliances. So Lovell was allowed to "squat" on the same field used by the University's botany department out at Jodrell Bank and to use some old military radar instruments. He did so well with these — particularly in tracking meteors during daylight — that more land was bought for him, and he was allowed to put up permanent laboratories.

In 1951, at the age of thirty-eight, he became the first holder of a newly founded chair or professorship of Radio Astronomy at Manchester University and Director of the Jodrell Bank Experimental Station.

That was when his struggles really began. He wanted a big, fully steerable radio telescope. But how was he to get it? Britain had hardly recovered from a very expensive war. Thousands of people were waiting for houses and factories to be rebuilt. They needed cars, clothes, shoes, and even food. Who had money for telescopes?

Lovell's first task was to convince the Royal Astronomical Society that the Big Dish was worthwhile. Then, when he had gotten their blessing, he had to raise the money. A government department, known as the Department of Industrial and Scientific Research, promised half the cost, which was then thought to be £400,000 ($1,120,000), and the Nuffield Foundation, which had been set up by Lord Nuffield, the famous automobile manufacturer, promised the balance.

Who was going to build the kind of telescope Lovell wanted? Lovell approached several engineers and asked them to suggest designs for a 250-foot steerable radio telescope. Some almost scoffed at the idea. Others said that it could not possibly be done for the money. Or they produced designs that were impracticable. The one exception was Henry Charles Husband, head of the engineering firm of the same name in the city of Sheffield, Yorkshire, famous for its steel and cutlery.

Lovell and Husband had discussed a giant telescope as far back as 1949. Lovell wanted a radio telescope that could point a sharp pencil-like receiving beam to any part of the sky in order to find the position of radio sources. Think what this means. Suppose, for example, we have an ordinary sight telescope standing on a flat piece of ground. To reach every part of the sky, it must be able to point horizontally north, east, south, and west, and to do this, it must swing around a vertical axis. But it must also be able to rise from the horizontal and point upward, at 5 degrees, 10 degrees, 45 degrees, or even 90 degrees, and any degrees in between — that is, vertically upward — moving for this purpose around a horizontal axis. So far, so good. But this horizontal-vertical or "altazimuth" mounting, as it is called, has a big disadvantage in a case where one particular star has to be followed, for stars do not pass across the sky in a straight line unless their course brings them right over the head of the observer. On the contrary, most of them, like the sun, to anyone north or south of the tropics, move in a curve. The result is that with an altazimuth telescope, each change in the position of the star requires an alteration to both the horizontal and the vertical position of the telescope at varying rates of change for each position throughout the day.

However, if one axis of the telescope is arranged so that it lies parallel to the axis of the earth running between the North and South Poles, then, once the telescope has been pointed at a given star, it will need to be swung around this one polar axis only, that is, on a plane parallel to the equator of the earth to keep the wanted star in sight as long as it can be seen above the horizon. And this "follow that star" maneuver can be attended to by a simple electric motor. A telescope arranged in this way is said to have an equatorial mounting.

Equatorially mounted telescopes have the extra advantage that the positions of all known stars are recorded in astronomers' tables according to their relation to the earth's axis on the day in question. So if you are using an equatorial telescope and want to find a star, you can learn from tables exactly how high the telescope should point and lock it into that position before proceeding with your east-west search. You could not, of course, do this with an ordinary altazimuth telescope, and this was one of the first big problems to face the designers of the Big Dish.

Once the decision was made to have a steerable radio telescope, it would theoretically have been better to have equatorial mounting for the Big Dish, instead of resting the bowl, as it stands now, on a turntable supported on the ground. But think of the extra difficulties and expense that would have been faced if the Big Dish had had an equatorial mounting. That part of England where it was proposed the Big Dish be built is approximately on latitude 53 degrees North. In other words, the whole apparatus would have had to be permanently tilted 53 degrees upward from the horizontal to lie parallel with the polar axis. Since, as it stands today, the Big Dish is the largest thing on wheels, imagine the stresses and strains and other difficulties that would have arisen if the whole apparatus had to be canted up at one end. Imagine trying to turn the whole apparatus around smoothly with the wheels going up and down the slope. The designers calculated that twice as much structural steel would be needed for an equatorial mounting. It would not be worth the effort or expense.

Fifty years ago it would have been impossible to solve the problem. But, today, we are in the age of the computer or calculating machine, which in a few months can do sums that would formerly have taken many hundreds of years with pencil and paper. Thus, information from tables can be fed into machines that use the answers to see that the telescope reaches the right position at the right moment. In other words, they can calculate for any position above the horizon how fast the radio telescope must move vertically and horizontally in order to track a radio star across the sky.

The machines make it possible for the Big Dish to have all the advantages of an equatorially mounted radio telescope and yet keep all its "feet" on the ground.

One of the difficulties faced by the designers was that the telescope had to be accurate at so many different speeds. Imagine, for example, a star seen just above the edge of the horizon passing in a gentle curve over the horizon. It might be possible to follow that by elevating and lowering the telescope one or two degrees in an hour.

But suppose you were placed in such a position that the star, as it rose, would pass directly overhead. To follow it, you would have to raise the telescope — and it makes no difference whether it is an eye telescope or a radio one — from zero degrees on the horizon to 90 degrees at the zenith and then lower the dish a further ninety degrees until the star sank again below the other horizon. Moreover, if the star were nearly but not exactly overhead, you would have to follow it very quickly with the azimuth part of the telescope as well.

Fortunately, it is only a small area of sky around the zenith where high speeds are required, and the only other time the telescope needs a fair turn of speed is when it is being set to pick up a star. It was decided, therefore, that it would be good enough if the telescope could turn through a complete circle both in azimuth and elevation in ten minutes. This means, in practice, a speed of only one mile an hour on the turntable.

In fact, it was the idea of slow speeds rather than high speeds that bothered the designers of the Big Dish. The slowest speed required meant that the Big Dish would have to move only one quarter of an inch in a minute. Would it be possible to shift 2,000 tons of movable parts at such a low speed without grunts and shudders?

And should they use an electric driving system or a hydraulic one? The Royal Navy had been very pleased with hydraulic drives used for aiming guns on battleships. If the same system could have been used for the telescope, then it might have been possible to cut out all electrical machinery on the telescope except for the radio transmitters and aerials, although electrical energy would still have been needed to build up the necessary hydraulic pressure and for the remote and automatic speed controls. But the designers came to the conclusion that the machinery needed to handle the telescope in gale conditions would have to be so big that the cost of providing it would be out of the question.

5

Designing the Big Dish

Engineers and scientists working together spent the next
two years roughing out a design for a radio telescope that
would do the job and still not cost a fantastic amount of
money.

A radio telescope with a metal reflector was considered
to be the ideal type, since it could be used both as a
transmitter and as a receiver. Moreover, if the dish could
be turned upside down without too much trouble, this, it
was thought, would allow the aerial to be changed for
different wave lengths by the ground staff without all the
bother of lowering them into the dish in the upturned
position. Every minute counts when using a radio telescope. An ordinary telescope, you see, can be serviced
during the day because is cannot then be used for seeing
stars. But a radio telescope is intended for use around
the clock both by day and by night, so that any time
spent on servicing it is time lost. So it was decided to

give the dish an electrically driven winch, which could lower the aerial as soon as the dish was upside down. The dish was also provided with an automatic device so that when the aerial was hoisted into place again, it would set in exactly the right position. However, even when locked into position, it would be possible to turn it around in order to improve reception.

At that time, both engineers and scientists were working in the dark, for the largest existing steerable radio telescope dishes were then about 50-feet across — although Professor Lovell already knew of the results obtained by

The Big Dish nearly upside down. A view taken after a new aerial had been installed to follow a U.S. moon probe. (British Information Service)

his own 220-foot *fixed* radio telescope. Lovell insisted that the new dish must be no smaller than 250 feet if any worthwhile advances were to be made in radio astronomy.

Lovell's original plan was to concentrate on wave lengths of between one meter and ten meters, in which range a large telescope would have outstanding advantages.

The next thing was to decide on the correct shape for the metal reflector. Several of the existing radio telescopes had been built with comparatively shallow bowls in order to save the expense of a large reflector. But, with a shallow, flattish bowl, you need a high aerial tower to pick up the rays reflected from the bowl, and this in turn means that the bowl has to carry extra weight (quite apart from the fact that a tall aerial is more difficult to get at when adjustments have to be made). Moreover, a shallow, unsheltered bowl picks up unwanted radio signals from all over the place. A deep, high-walled bowl, on the other hand, cuts down interference and the confusion caused by the changes in interference that occur when the telescope is moved from one position to another. So it was decided to make a deep bowl, focusing on an aerial level with the top of the bowl.

This also fitted in best with the idea of reaching the aerial from the ground by inverting the bowl, for if the aerial did not project above the edge of the dish, then the horizontal axis of the dish could be that much nearer the ground.

Incidentally, it is perhaps worth pointing out that a

fixed telescope gains less than one might expect from having a commanding position. The owner may prefer to be protected from all stray man-made radio impulses. In fact, the Russians have gotten excellent results from a dish-type radio telescope made by digging a hole in the ground and lining it with reflecting material. Of course, such a telescope, though cheap to build, is a fixed-view one and not steerable. With a steerable telescope, horizon-looking may be desirable for tracking satellites, for detecting (and afterward cutting out) man-made interference, and for picking up long-distance interferometer signals.

Next, after the shape of the Big Dish had been decided, there was the problem of what it should be made of. Jodrell Bank already had a *small* steerable radio telescope in use, and its reflector had originally been made of chicken wire. Later, the chicken wire had been replaced by closely spaced metal latticework, which had already been used successfully in the United States, the Netherlands, and Germany. But it was found that, if the holes in the mesh were bigger than two inches square, the smaller, shorter radio waves of around one meter leaked through undetected. If the mesh was small enough to catch these waves, it would also catch and hold ice and snow, which not only prevent a reflector from working properly but pull it out of shape. Moreover, radio waves could penetrate from underneath the dish, where of course there are no stars, to reach the aerial.

Another trouble was that, in winter, the exposed parts of the mesh would ice up first, making the telescope top-heavy and difficult to control when the wind blew on the solid wall of ice. And even without icing conditions, a strong wind could start the mesh vibrating, which would affect the accuracy of the recordings. So the engineers decided to redesign the new telescope to make a solid dish in spite of the extra weight and expense that this would involve.

Aluminum, used in a radio telescope at the Naval Research Laboratory in Washington, was one possibility. It would have been nice and light to work with — but probably too brittle for a really large telescope. Moreover, the lower-priced aluminum alloys expanded so much under heat that the Big Dish might not have kept its true shape during the hot summer months; and the good alloys were far too expensive. Instead, it was decided to have a skin of steel welded to a surrounding framework. With this arrangement the surface of the reflector would help to reinforce the framework holding it. Steel does not expand too much in summer or contract in winter; it has a certain amount of elasticity, and its very weight could be used as ballast to keep the structure steady.

The designers' first plan for the Big Dish had been to support the bowl of the dish on a broad circular girder projecting outward from the rim of the dish. This plan would have been excellent if the dish had always been looking upward at the sky. But since it was considered important to be able to turn the dish upside down so that the aerial could easily be changed, this idea had to be dropped.

Next came a plan for putting a heavy rocker-shaped girder under the dish to support it. A scheme was actually worked out for assembling this girder with the curved part as near the ground as possible. Later it would have been possible to build the dish upside down with the curved part uppermost and the rest of the structure filled in like the spokes of an umbrella.

But when the engineers came to analyze the stresses and strains that a telescope made in this way would have to bear, they decided that although it would work very well on the one-meter wave length (for which it had originally been intended), the dish would not be sufficiently rigid for work on the 21-centimeter wave length.

The astronomers did not allow very much latitude. Their requirement was that when there was no wind, the dish — almost as big as a football field — must be true to within five inches of what it should be. But even when there was wind, rain, ice, and snow, the bowl must not give more than another three inches, and it must be safe and controllable with wind up to a hundred miles per hour. (That does not mean that they planned to carry out work during a gale, and in practice the telescope is closed down when average wind speeds are greater than *37 m.p.h.*)

There was little doubt in Husband's mind that the telescope would stand up all right even against winds of more than one hundred miles per hour. But how best to hold the shape of the bowl?

Eventually a strong framework was constructed in the

space underneath the dish on each side. The axle on which the dish swings up and down is set near to the bottom of the bowl.

Mr. Husband made a special study of how the dish would behave when it was turned upward from the horizon to the polestar. He found that when the open part of the dish was trained on the horizon, a considerable part of it would tend to slump downward because of the pull of the earth's gravity. He also concluded that if a way could be found to keep the edge of the bowl circular and flat, then the main distortion could be limited to a comparatively small area at the center of the bottom of the dish, which would be slightly deeper when the dish was looking upward than when it was facing the horizon. The rim was eventually stiffened with the help of a deep collar and sixteen supports connected to a central hub. Stresses and strains had to be worked out for the dish, and those calculations had to take into account not only the weight of the structure itself and any snow and ice it might collect but also the effect of the wind from all points of the compass at all angles of the telescope and at all speeds of movement.

These were particularly difficult in the case of the framework connecting the dish with the two towers that were to support it. Calculations had also to be made for every one of the thousands of supports underneath the bowl itself. A computing machine was kept busy for a whole year.

At each stage one problem tangled with another. For

example, it might be necessary, in order to make the reflector firmer and truer, to alter the structure supporting the bowl, which in turn would affect the balance of the telescope when tilted so that new arrangements for controlling the tilting of the dish would be required. And so on.

The next question was how to steer the telescope. Lovell and his team had made it clear that the telescope must move horizontally or vertically at speeds ranging from 2 degrees in the hour to 36 degrees per minute, the second speed being roughly 1,000 times the other. But that was not all. They wanted to be able to move the telescope horizontally and vertically at different speeds at the same time. And they not only wanted to be able to follow a star automatically by allowing for the movement of the earth, but they also asked to be able to scan a given area around a star or a given "rectangle" of sky. They also wanted to be able to lock the telescope in any position.

We shall see in time how all this was managed. Only one thing was certain. It had never been done before. Never before had something a good deal larger than the dome of St. Paul's Cathedral in London and weighing 2,000 tons been designed to move so delicately.

It had been decided that the most practical way would be for the bowl to be held above the ground by two towers — one standing on each side. If these towers were mounted on railway lines curved into a circle, the reflector could be swung from left to right, or the other way around, all the way around the horizon . . . north, east, south, or west.

But even the foundations were none too easy to lay.

The surveyors began by boring for samples of the under-lying soil. They found that the topsoil of the site where they intended to put the telescope was a mixed lot. Some parts held more water than others. So they started to bore deeper and deeper in the search for a more reliable foundation. They got down twenty feet, thirty feet, forty feet . . . and still there was no sign of anything firm. What was wanted was a layer of soil that would carry the weight of the telescope at rest and would not be disturbed by the twisting movement of 2,000 tons of metal as the instru-ment turned.

Not until they reached between seventy and eighty feet did they find a layer of Keuper marl (clay) on which they could rely. Stones for the foundations had to be sunk to this level for a start. It was like burying a ten-story block of apartments in a hole in the ground. In the end, 10,000 tons of concrete had to be used.

The rails that were to lie on this foundation would obviously have to be immensely strong to avoid the risk of bending and buckling. So the type chosen was the heav-iest available, each yard weighing nearly 112 pounds. They would have to be true so that they could be laid level, and they would have to be free of flaws. If the rails were not absolutely smooth, it would be difficult to avoid starts and jerks as the telescope moved around. It was de-cided that they must not vary by more than one-sixteenth of an inch.

The designers chose to use four rings of rails each in-side the other, the outer two rails being 17 feet from the inner. The base of each of the towers supporting the two edges of the dish would therefore be 17 feet across, and the distance between the two towers carrying the dish between them would be something like 100 yards.

When one looks down from above, the structure carrying the bowl looks like an enormous squat "H." Each of the outer four corners of the uprights of this "H" is provided with a set of wheels in pairs like the bogie wheels in front of a railway steam engine. These wheels are designed to run on the outer two circles of rail. The inner four corners of the uprights of the "H" are also provided with sets of bogies, which fit exactly onto the two inner

The Big Dish on its turntable. Two of the supporting bogie assemblies are shown, left and center, and, on the right, one of the driving engines. (British Information Service)

circles of rail. From above, the telescope on its rails looks like an "H" pivoting around on top of an "O." These eight sets of bogies are mainly for steadying the Big Dish against the sudden assaults of the wind.

The actual driving mechanism is separate. Under each of the towers are eight wheels, four on each of the inner two rails. The four driving engines are fixed to an extension of the center bar of the "H" on each side. One other refinement has been introduced to the telescope. It might have been copied from nature. Bird watchers have long ago noticed that the eggs of birds that nest on the bare ledges of cliffs are conical in shape rather than round. This is a very convenient arrangement because a conical egg, if blown by the wind, tends to roll around in a circle, keeping the pointed end of the egg in the middle, instead of rolling over and over and over the side of the cliff. (The explanation is that the larger end of the egg automatically travels farther during each revolution than the smaller.)

The cliff-egg principle has been used at Jodrell Bank to make the telescope turn more smoothly. All the wheels running on the rails are slightly cone-shaped with the imaginary point or apex of the cone being something like 50 yards away. It may sound unnecessary, but it makes all the difference.

The rails and the driving motors are not the only things that control the part of the compass to which the telescope points. On the ground, in the center of the cross bar of the "H" is a kind of turntable revolving around a short post or stump. The towers and the whole framework support-

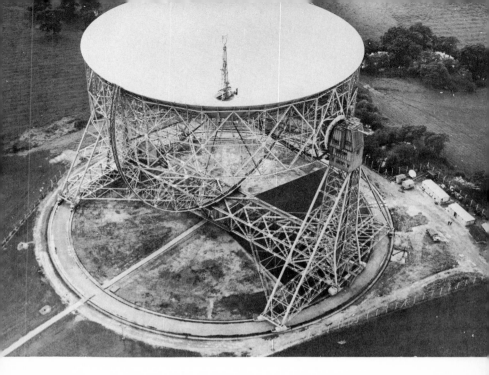

Aerial view of the Big Dish turntable with the telescope pointing at the zenith. (Keystone)

ing the dish pivot around this post. The main purpose of the post itself is to take the sideways thrust of the wind. And for the same reason, the bogies are equipped with anchors, which can be let down during stormy weather to prevent the structure from being lifted off the ground by the violence of the wind.

After arrangements were made for the Big Dish to be swung horizontally, the next problem was how to tilt the Big Dish so that it could stare either at the horizon or right up at the polestar.

And here Professor Patrick Blackett of Manchester University, winner of a Nobel prize for research into atomic physics, had a real brain wave. He had seen how perfectly naval guns were controlled in large battleships. "Why not use the same mechanism for a telescope?" he asked himself.

Now it happened that, at this time, two battleships, *Royal Sovereign* and *Revenge,* were being broken up, and part of their fittings were two enormous cogged circular racks and pinions each 27 feet across. These had been used for aiming the ships' 15-inch guns. Husband hurried off to the naval base at Inverkeithing in Scotland and inspected them. They were in perfect condition, and he boldly decided to include this secondhand material in his treasured telescope.

As a matter of fact, the same equipment, if it had been specially made for the job, would have been far outside Husband's budget, whereas, being secondhand, it came well within it. One great feature of these racks was that, being circular, they would allow the telescope to be turned upside down — which was just what was needed when the aerial had to be changed.

These circular racks could be installed at each end of the horizontal axis of the telescope and connect their teeth with the cogs of the driving motor.

So far then, we have seen how the designers planned the foundations for the telescope, how the dish was to be carried and moved horizontally and vertically, and how the material was chosen from which the bowl was to be built.

One of the cogged racks, taken from a British battleship, that allow the Big Dish to turn vertically through 360 degrees. (British Information Service)

One other clever idea, called the bicycle wheel, has been introduced in order to steady the big dish. The bicycle wheel is really a kind of circular hoop that runs underneath the dish at right angles to the telescope's horizontal axis. Of course, it is not a complete wheel. It starts at the lip of the Big Dish, runs down almost to the ground, and then up the other side of the dish to the opposite rim. At the point where the bicycle wheel comes nearest to the base of the telescope, engineers have fixed two groups of wheels, each fitted with pneumatic tires. As the telescope turns, the rim of the bicycle wheel runs over these tires, which can be blown up or even jacked up to allow them to get a better grip on the wheel.

The tire wheels are sprung to help smooth out the movement of the telescope. A braking device can also be

The Big Dish during construction, showing the hanging laboratory below the bowl and, at the bottom of the photograph, the motor house. (British Information Service)

applied to the edge of the bicycle wheel to keep the telescope steady in high winds. The rest of the structure carrying the dish consists of a lattice-steel cradle. From the center of the bowl, there rises a tower 55 feet high, as tall as a four-story house. And on top of this tower, 62½ feet above the bottom of the dish, is the aerial. Here the messages coming from the remote regions of outer space are received.

But we have not exhausted the wonders of the Big Dish. In the middle, right below the center of the bowl, is a workshop or, to be more exact, a laboratory. At first, one wonders whether perhaps it was right to put a laboratory there. It adds to the weight that has to be raised when the dish is turned on its side. However, the laboratory is used to amplify the signals received by the aerial, and if it had been located on the ground, away from the telescope, these signals might have had to travel along a considerable length of wire, which would have weakened them. So it is better after all to have the laboratory as near to the aerial as possible.

The laboratory has, of course, to be specially suspended so that the floor stays level when the telescope swings from one position to another.

The laboratory has also been fitted with a wind-damping device to guard against sudden gusts of wind that could otherwise set it swinging and make the crew seasick. You can reach the laboratory by climbing a staircase or walk running right from one side of the underneath portion of the bowl to the other.

Now you have a general idea of the main design of the

telescope. You also know how the main features came to be decided in some cases, in advance, while others were worked out after the construction had already been started. As we shall see in a moment, it is one thing to design a telescope and quite another to build it.

6

Putting the Big Dish Together

The arrangements for building the Jodrell Bank telescope were so complex that no one contractor big enough to handle the job could be found. Thirty different firms had to be signed up by Manchester University — some to supply ready-made parts, others to put the parts together, and others again to place them in their right position in the structure of the telescope.

This division of work was perhaps just as well because it allowed the engineers far more freedom to change their minds and adopt new ideas than they would have had if they had signed up right at the beginning with a single firm. Where possible, the designers tried to save costs by using ready-built parts, but many of the components of the telescope had to be specially designed for a particular job, and more than a thousand different drawings were needed.

The rails were rolled from a brand-new rolling mill and

turned out so well that the depth of the rails varied by less than one sixteenth of an inch. Once the rails had been made, they had to be laid. First, at their base, came a layer of fine concrete "chips" crushed down so that they stood firm after 28 days' pounding under a pressure of 10,000 pounds per square inch. Then came a layer of steel bed plates carefully laid and leveled. Then came the rails themselves. The joins between the rails were quite different from those you see on ordinary railway lines, where there is quite a wide gap between each length of rail. Instead, each section of rail was tapered at each end in the shape of a wedge so that the join between them is a long and gentle slope ending in a wafer-thin edge. This tapering made it possible to get a really smooth join. At one time the engineers thought that they might have to use a surface-grinding machine to polish off the joins, but only in a few cases did the use of the machine prove necessary.

As a means of cutting down the vibration, no two joins in the four circles of rails are put alongside one another. Thus, the smallest possible number of wheels on the rails are affected by any one join. All the tracks are held down by bolts, which can easily be reached if there are replacements to be made or if the level has to be altered.

There is one other smart trick that the engineers used in order to make the telescope turn smoothly on its rails. The axles of the wheels on the driving bogies are not parallel to each other in the way that they are on an ordinary railway engine. On the contrary, each axle points directly at the central pivot of the telescope, which again lowers the friction.

The extra trouble taken by the engineers on these finer points turned out to be worthwhile. Friction losses have been reduced to about one-third of 1 per cent, and as long as the wind does not blow hard, it needs only one-third of a single horsepower to turn the telescope around to any point of the compass. Therefore, the telescope, weighing 2,000 tons, can be turned around (once it has been started) with the same ordinary battery that you use for the self-starter of a family car. In fact, everything runs so smoothly that for someone standing on the bowl, it is impossible to tell whether the telescope is at rest or has started moving.

Even less power is needed to tilt the bowl (because one side partly balances the other), and the main resistance is from the tires of the bicycle wheel on the lower side of the dish.

The new design that had been adopted in order that the telescope might carry out research on the 21-centimeter wave length meant that a different method of construction had to be used. Instead of building the bowl like an umbrella, with the dome of the dish uppermost, it was thought better to go about the job with the dish open to the sky.

First came the rails and the lower turntable part of the telescope, the two towers to support the dish, and then the "bridge" connecting the two towers.

One of the most difficult parts of the framework from the designers' point of view was the pieces connecting the lip of the dish to the horizontal axis on which it had to swing. It is here that the force of the wind concentrates,

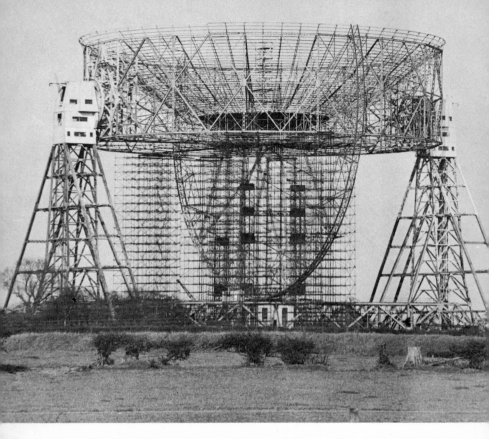

The Big Dish and its scaffolding, 130 feet high, in position during construction. (Keystone)

as though it were trying to twist the whole dish from its supports.

When the towers and the support for the horizontal axis, worked by gun racks from battleships, had been completed, it was time to start work on the dish itself. Metal scaffolding reaching 130 feet into the sky was built at the points where the sixteen main panels of the dish were to join, and a central scaffolding tower was also erected on which to build the hub from which the girders supporting the dish would spread out.

Then, starting from the two towers, the circular ring girder to support the outer edge of the dish was built and connected section by section to the center hub. Finally the reflecting surface of the dish was put in place inside the framework.

As an additional precaution, all the important girders both in the tower structure and in the bowl framework were fitted up with gauges to record the strains to which they are subjected in operation.

Welders and platers add the reflecting surface to the Big Dish after the framework has been completed. (Keystone)

But before the designers could sit back with a sigh of relief, they had to be sure that the shape of the bowl was what it was supposed to be. How could they check it?

Of course, the width and the depth could be measured, but that would not tell whether or not the curve were true all the way around or whether it had sagged like a middle-aged waistline. But scientists recognized at least three possible ways of taking the measurements. One is to reflect rays of light into the bowl from certain reference points. Then, if the bowl is true, the reflection of the light will exactly strike another point, the position of which has been worked out in advance.

A second method is to make a similar trial with short-wave radio waves bounced off the reflector in the same way as radar waves are bounced off the moon.

But the engineers decided that they could make all the tests they wanted in a simpler way — with measuring wires. Not that this method was easy! There were special difficulties when the bowl was tilted (as it had to be, to make sure that the dish stayed in shape whichever way it was turned). Also, when the weather was bad and the wind gusty, the men near the top of the dish had to work as carefully as steeple jacks.

But the final results were rewarding. As the dish was lowered from the zenith, or point directly above the observer, to the horizon, the focus of the whole apparatus altered by only two inches.

The designers realized that the aerial, sharply pointed into the air, would be an invitation to lightning to strike in the same place twice. So a special instrument was installed in the control room to give warning of "thunder in the air" or any other electrical change in the atmosphere so that the crew could take all precautions. When thunderstorms are around, all painters and maintenance men are taken off the telescope, for if lightning struck, even if these men were not themselves hit, they might be startled into losing a foothold or dropping their equipment. But the most vulnerable part of the telescope as far as lightning is concerned is not the aerial or the structure or indeed the machinery, but the bearings on which the telescope swings. If these were damaged, a very costly and time-consuming repair job would surely be needed. So lightning conductors — made of copper tubing, which is more attractive to lightning than the steel structure of the telescope — have been installed to decoy the lightning away from the bearings. The electric wiring, too, is protected by earthing plates, which allow any lightning strike to pass straight down to earth without damaging the installation. The circular tracks on which the telescope turns are also earthed at many points with copper "tapes" and so is the central pivot.

It was also important to prevent large quantities of water from collecting in the bowl. Otherwise, it would be possible to turn the dish into a handsome swimming pool or even a sailing club. Accordingly, holes have been made in the bottom of the dish so that water runs through them at any angle the dish takes.

Aircraft warning lights are another refinement fitted

to the telescope; they are mounted on the highest parts of the girders.

Perhaps you wonder how much the Big Dish finally cost? To some extent the whole project was a labor of love, inasmuch as the radio astronomers who helped to build the telescope were earning far less than they could have done in the commercial world — and were paid no overtime.

In the years just after the war, money did not go as far as it was supposed to. The price of steel rose. The cost of rivets rose. Wages rose, and the standards of accomplishment expected from the telescope rose, too, for in order to detect the movement of hydrogen clouds in space, it was decided that the telescope must be able to work on the relatively short wave length of 21 centimeters, which, in turn, meant that new and more expensive methods of building had to be used.

The result was that the cost, instead of working out at £400,000, as originally estimated, was more . . . much more.

Lovell needed an extra £300,000 ($840,000). The Government, which by then had become his convinced supporter, dug into its pockets and offered to supply half of the extra money. This left £150,000 ($420,000) still to be collected.

Lovell went canvassing. He called on private sources, on industrial firms, and even arranged to hire out the telescope on a part-time basis to the United States Government. And so the last of the deficit was wiped out.

The whole bill was in the neighborhood of £700,000 ($1,960,000). Excluding the site, the radio receiving and transmitting equipment, and the professional fees, the total came to £559,670 (a little more than one and a half million dollars). Some of the items that might have been expected to cost a great deal came out cheap and vice versa.

For example, those exploratory borings, when they had to dig down to 90 feet to see what kind of soil they were dealing with, cost only £370 (a little over $1,000) — equivalent to about a dozen men's time for three weeks without counting anything for the use of the machinery and many other expenses that no doubt cropped up.

On the other hand, painting the inside of the dish to help it reflect radio waves came to £5,000 ($14,000).

The railway tracks, stretching for something like half a mile in all and true to a fraction of an inch, cost £11,000 ($30,800).

One of the most important items was a device that is not in use anywhere on the telescope — namely the experimental wind tunnel. This, together with the strain gauges, experimental membrane, and electrical and heat reflecting experiments, came to £2,000 ($5,600).

Supplying and putting up the steel work for holding the dish, painting it, providing the aluminum cladding for the three-story motor rooms and laboratories in each tower, the motor generator house, and the suspended laboratory worked out at £270,000 ($756,000) — about half the total (exclusive of site, receiving and transmitting equipment, and professional fees). The bearings and wind-damping device for the suspended laboratory took another £700 ($1,960). The adjustable aerial carrier came to £1,000 ($2,800). The electrical and mechanical driving equipment worked out at £5,000 ($14,000) — about one tenth of the total.

The surface of the dish cost £15,000 ($42,000), exactly the same as the electric cables, including the airplane warning lights. The control system, control desk, and computer were nearly as expensive at £14,000 ($39,200).

It cost £4,500 ($12,600) to build the roads for the site and to install the drains. Arrangements for draining the dish itself took another £2,500 ($7,000), and the lifts and hoists came to £6,500 ($18,200).

By 1957 the telescope was ready to take part in the International Geophysical Year program, during which the nations of the world agreed to pool their discoveries with one another. Four years later Lovell was knighted by Queen Elizabeth for his successful work.

7

Getting It to Work

About half of the 75 people — almost all men — working at Jodrell Bank are engineers who keep the instrument with its power plant and other accessories in working order.

The telescope is generally in use for about 16 out of 24 hours of the day — leaving eight hours for maintenance, which includes operations such as testing, changing the aerial, painting, installing fresh cables, and the like. Since the telescope began its full-scale work in October, 1957, the engineers have discovered new ways of keeping it going. For example, in order to reduce the stresses and strains, the telescope is no longer automatically turned upside down when the aerial is changed. Instead, a man is sent up from the bowl to the top of the aerial by means of a kind of portable chain hoist, and at least one piece of equipment has been taken out of the Big Dish by means of a helicopter.

Before any work begins on the telescope, the radio equipment is given a special check. For this purpose, a big radio source whose position is known is chosen, and the telescope is set to point at that position. Then, if the correct radio response arrives from the star, the research men know that the Big Dish is ready to work.

This brings us to the question, "What is the telescope mainly used for?"

The answer is that a general program of work is thought out well in advance. Astronomers are at present groping for the answer to certain questions about the nature of the universe, and the Big Dish is specially designed as the finest instrument for tackling a number of these questions in its own particular way. Obviously, there is no point in Jodrell Bank carrying out work that is being done perfectly well somewhere else. All this has to be taken into consideration before a work program is laid down. And also the program may have to be revised in a hurry if some new development — such as Sputnik I in 1957 — comes into the field. The research staff consists of about 36 men, 12 of whom are permanently at Jodrell Bank, the other two dozen being young graduate scientists taking courses in radio astronomy. There are usually half a dozen investigations going on at the same time, and each project is tackled by a team of about six.

At present, the general plan is to devote approximately one-third of the telescope's working time to separating and classifying radio sources in the sky and to measuring their angular size. This is all part of the job of learning how radio impulses are produced and where they come from. It will help to make radio surveys carried out by interferometer radio telescopes (which reject wide-angle sources and take only narrow-angle sources) agree with those carried out by the dish-type telescopes. It will help to answer questions such as: "Are all radio sources of a certain minimum size?" "Do some sources seem smaller to us than others because we are looking at the sharp end of a galaxy or group of galaxies that is really a big balloon or sausage-shaped cluster?" "If an apparently small source gives out a signal, does it follow that the source is farther away than a larger source giving a signal of the same strength?" "Are the sources expanding in size?"

It may take four or five years to get some of the answers to these questions.

The Big Dish, too, is being used as an interferometer in order to measure the width of these radio sources. It has gone into partnership with a movable radio telescope. This movable telescope is linked with Jodrell Bank but set up at varying distances from it. At one time the two instruments were half a mile apart. At other times they have been three miles apart, twelve miles, 40 miles (in the Welsh Hills), and even in Lincolnshire, 70 miles away from Jodrell Bank, on the other side of England.

Of course, it would not be worth wiring up the movable telescope with Jodrell Bank to make an interferometer when the two are so far apart, for this would mean hiring an expensive landline from the post office. So the information received by the roving telescope is sent back to

Jodrell Bank by microwave radio, that is, a radio using a very short wave length. When using microwaves, the transmitter and the receiver have to be within sight of each other. So when the message has to be sent from Lincolnshire across the Pennine hills to Jodrell Bank, the scientists make use of the British Broadcasting Corporation equipment, which has been set up at Holme Moss on top of the ridge from where an observer can see both Cheshire and Lincolnshire. A relay device within sight of the roving telescope in Lincolnshire picks up the microwaves and relays them on to Jodrell Bank in Cheshire. And all this is done without the need for a human operator.

If you average out the radio telescope's working hour, another ten minutes of it is taken up with surveying the Milky Way, and a regular map has been prepared, showing which parts of the Milky Way are strong from a radio point of view and which are weak. The map looks something like those you see in geography books to show the heights of mountains or the depths of oceans, and we shall see later that it is prepared in a very interesting way. It is being carried out on two different frequencies of 240 megacycles and 480 megacycles per second.

Another six minutes in the hour is being spent on investigating the magnetic influences among the stars that could affect the navigation of space ships. Another six minutes is devoted to studies of hydrogen cloud, revealed by their signals on the 21-centimeter wave length — studies that help to map the heavens more accurately and, within limits, to calculate the speed of movement of its various parts.

Some of the telescope's time is spent in bouncing radio echoes off the moon because, by doing so, it is possible to find out more and more about the layers through which the radio impulses pass.

In another, more straightforward piece of research, the Big Dish is being used to determine more accurately the

An especially clear view of the "bicycle wheel," the device that adds stability to the Big Dish. At this moment the telescope was pointing toward the moon. (British Information Service)

distances between the planets in the solar system. One is apt to take it for granted when one reads that the earth is 93 million miles from the sun that this is really the exact distance. But, of course, this is only an approximate figure because of the very great distances involved. Efforts have been made at various times to cut down the margin of error. If one could only be absolutely certain of the distance from the earth to any of the members of the solar system, then we should be on much firmer ground with the others, since we already know the ratios between the distances of the remaining planets with an accuracy of better than one part in a million.

Eros, one of the minor planets, comes comparatively close to the earth at times, and one astronomer worked on and off for twenty years, taking observations of its position in order to work out its distance from the earth. After all this time he reckoned that his findings were accurate only to within 20,000 miles. But using Venus, the Big Dish was able to get results ten times as accurate in two years. In other words, the margin of error for the position of Eros was cut down from 20,000 miles to 2,000 miles.

Although the telescope spends less than three minutes per working hour on tracking man-made satellites, it was satellites that first made Jodrell Bank familiar to millions who might never have understood the meaning of its more important, long-term work.

Russia sent up the first artificial satellite on October

4, 1957, and although there was no man aboard, or even an animal, the event caused a tremendous sensation. It was, after all, the first object to be thrown beyond the earth's atmosphere that did not at once return to earth — and it was circling the earth once every one and a half hours, at a height of some 560 miles and at the tremendous speed of more than 18,000 miles per hour, and sending out radio messages at the same time. Nor was this all. The Sputnik or traveler, as it was soon called, contained instruments and a radio transmitter. These instruments were sensitive to light and heat, and they altered the wave length and rhythm of the Sputnik's radio signals whenever conditions changed inside the satellite. But it was difficult to be sure how long the radio signals would continue or how long the satellite would pursue its chosen path.

These radio signals were sent out on two different frequencies, and it was quite possible for amateurs to pick up the signals for themselves.

As long as the satellite kept up its speed, the force of gravity of the earth pulling it downward was balanced by the urge of the satellite to fly outward into space. But eventually friction was bound to slow down the Sputnik and so draw it back to the earth again.

Now the Jodrell Bank telescope, being a transmitter as well as a receiver, might be able to track the satellite by radar even if it stopped giving radio signals (which might easily happen if the radio failed while the satellite

A night shot of the Big Dish taken while the telescope was tracking Russia's first Sputnik. (David Moore, Camera Press, London)

was still in orbit or on its way back to the earth). It might also be able to track the rocket that took the satellite into orbit, even though the rocket had separated from the Sputnik and was sending out no radio signals.

When the news of the first satellite "broke," painters were still in the bowl of the Big Dish, making ready for the telescope's official trials. Some of the cables had still to be linked up. No one could have expected that it would have to go into action without any preliminary warning. But within a week, Lovell was able to start tracking the satellite and its rocket and, on a later occasion, succeeded in finding the rocket when it was still a thousand miles from Britain and in quite a different position from the one the Russians believed it occupied. Eventually the Big Dish was able to establish when the rocket began to drop, as it met with resistance from gas and dust, even 500 miles above the earth. In March, 1958, the Big Dish was also able to record the decline of the Russian Sputnik II (the one that carried the dog Laika) and its fall on April 14 after the batteries had failed. The news of Lovell's success soon reached the United States, where plans to send up satellites were already under way. The experts came to the conclusion that Jodrell Bank offered them their best chance of keeping track of their own space probes.

The experiments in which the Americans were most interested were carried out under the code name of Pioneer. The Pioneers were, in fact, among the first attempts to circle the sun and moon. Pioneer I was an 83-pound satellite launched on October 11, 1958, toward the moon, and with the aid of the Jodrell Bank telescope, it was tracked up to a height of 60,000 miles. Pioneer IV, another satellite, was followed to a distance of 400,000 miles, and Pioneer V, which was sent into orbit around the sun in March, 1960, was tracked for nearly 23 million miles, and Lovell was personally thanked by President Eisenhower for his work.

Meanwhile, a new development showed that the radio telescope at Jodrell Bank would not, after all, have to remain blind for the whole of its life. On August 7, 1959, the U.S. Explorer VI sent back the first pictures by radio from outer space.

But it was once again the Russians who provided the Big Dish with its biggest thrill. That was in September, 1959, when the Russian Lunik II was launched. It left the earth on a Saturday, traveling at seven miles a second. The following night soon after midnight Moscow Radio announced that Lunik II had hit the moon and that the first space flight from one celestial body to another had therefore been completed. The men at the Big Dish believe that they got the only independent evidence that Lunik II had, in fact, hit the moon.

You may possibly have heard the whistle sent out by Lunik II or a recording of it. It sounded like a series of blasts on a whistle, the kind of whistle that makes a trilling noise because it has a piece of cork or a dried pea inside it. The Russians had said that the satellite was due to hit the moon at exactly a minute past ten o'clock British Summer Time. If that happened, the whistling would stop.

A number of the staff at Jodrell Bank were listening. Ten o'clock came with the satellite whistling. Another minute passed with the sound continuing. Then another minute as the clock showed two minutes past ten. Twenty-three seconds later there was an uncanny silence. Lunik

II had ended its journey of 240,000 miles more punctually than many short-distance trains.

There were a few people — and perhaps there still are — who say that Lunik II did not really hit the moon but that the Russians had fixed things so that the radio would stop transmitting at about ten o'clock on that Sunday evening. But the men at the Big Dish have evidence to the contrary. They had been tracking Lunik and noticed that over the last half hour of its flight the frequency of the wave length on which it was sending out changed in the very way it could have been expected to change when the satellite began to be affected by the gravity pull of the moon and increased its speed of travel accordingly. Moreover, accurate tracking allowed the Jodrell Bank experts to work out that Lunik II hit the moon very close to its center.

Another interesting but less conclusive episode occurred in February, 1961, when the Russians tried to send a satellite to Venus. It left on February 12 on its immensely long journey, and in order to make the batteries last as long as possible it was due to send signals only once every five days. All went well on February 17, the first day when the signals were due. But the Russians apparently felt that they needed a second opinion. On February 21, the day before the next series of signals was due, they sent tracking information to Jodrell Bank with a request that the telescope be used to pick up the satellite's next batch of signals. But at the appointed time no signals came.

Once again the Big Dish waited for five days, and once

again the telescope was pointed at the spot where the satellite should have been on February 27. Again nothing.

But the men at Jodrell Bank did not give up the hunt. There was always a chance that the satellite would begin once more to "sing," as radio men call it. On May 17, when the satellite should have been homing on Venus, Jodrell Bank's giant saucer was turned in that direction and a search carried out in the most likely sector. Faint sounds were heard. And on the nineteenth and twentieth of May, the same sounds were picked up again. But without more information from the Russians, it was impossible to be certain whether these could have come from the satellite or whether it was a false trail, so Lovell got in touch with the Russians and told them what he had heard at Jodrell Bank.

He said he had come to the conclusion that the radio impulses picked up at Jodrell Bank were not inconsistent with the Soviet space ship on its way to Venus. The Russians apparently agreed, too, for one of their top scientists soon got through on the telephone. The scientist turned out to be a woman speaking almost perfect English. Alla Masevitch, still under forty, is professor of astrophysics at Moscow University. She told Lovell, "We are very interested in the details you have sent us. Would it be possible for me to come over to Jodrell Bank, see the recordings you have, and try to follow them up with the help of the radio telescope?" Lovell at once gave his consent. And so, for the first time, a Russian actually worked at Jodrell Bank.

This story has no proper ending, because no one was

able to prove that the signals had, in fact, come from a Russian satellite on its way to Venus and because no one was able to detect any further signals. The U. S. probe, Mariner II, sent to Venus in the autumn of 1962, "spoke" more clearly, and the radio telescope at Jodrell Bank was able to collect five miles of tape recordings from it to send to America.

If the research groups had nothing else to do but point the telescope here and there, they would all be falling over themselves and fighting one another to be allowed to use it. Fortunately, the radio sources they want to investigate don't all appear in the sky at the same time and — far more important — each research team has to spend a great deal of time interpreting the meaning of what the telescope tells them.

All that the telescope normally provides is a wavy line on squared graph paper and the time and date at which the record was made. Just think what has to be added before anything can be made of this record. First — where was the telescope pointing at the time? Was it locked or was it moving? Is the map reference of the spot to which it was pointing to be related to a star map of the whole visible sky or to a large-scale map of the Milky Way?

All kinds of other possibilities have to be considered as well. For example, in astronomy all observations are in theory taken from the center of the earth. But Jodrell Bank is nowhere near the center of the earth. Then, too, the apparent direction from which the radio waves appear to have come may not, because of the earth's movement, be the true direction — just as when you put your head out of a moving railway carriage window, the wind always seems to be coming from the front of the train, though this may not be its true direction. Again, the radio waves may have been "bent" during their journey through the earth's atmosphere. So all sorts of calculations are required before the information collected by the Big Dish makes sense.

It is said that it takes a trained scientist twenty minutes to work out the position at which an altazimuth telescope should point in order to intercept a given star at a given instant of time. Imagine how difficult it would be to keep up with the radio telescope during, say, a whole hour. In practice, the work has to be done by machinery. The information shown on the telescope graph is first "translated" onto a tape of the kind that you see in an ordinary tape recorder, only this tape is not designed for making noise. Instead, it has holes punched on it in various patterns. Thus, if the line penned by the telescope shows a sharp rise at one point, the holes on the tape will be arranged in a certain pattern to show this, and so on. Now let us suppose, as we did earlier, that you are making a radio map of the Milky Way. For this purpose the telescope will have been doing what is called "box scanning," that is, it will have been going over the Milky Way piece by piece like a patchwork quilt, working to and fro across each piece sweeping up one row, across and down the next.

When making this map, you want to know exactly where the telescope was pointing during each instant of its journey. The answer is once again given by machine. The spot at which the telescope was pointing during each instant of time can also be represented by holes punched on a tape, and both these tapes can be fed together into a machine that links the information together. It would have taken weeks or even months to get the same results with pencil and paper, even if the scan had been a comparatively short one.

It is even possible to color your radio map of the Milky Way according to the strength of the signals received from it, with the faint signals in yellow, perhaps, medium signals in various shades of light and medium brown, and strong signals in dark brown. To distinguish these areas from each other, you will have to fill in hundreds and perhaps thousands of positions. If you had been doing the work by hand, you would have had to look at the wavy line provided by the telescope to see at what point it rose above a certain height. You would then have had to work out where the telescope must have been pointing at the time and transfer the result to the map — eventually joining all the points of equal strength to provide the boundaries of the various areas of color.

However, when using a machine, or computer as it is called, you merely feed in the two punched tapes, giving the readings of the telescope and the position at which it was pointing, and also a third tape punched with holes indicating the questions you would like answered. This third tape is called the program tape and is white in color to distinguish it from the other two, which are red and green.

Using the program tape, you can ask the computer to tell you the position at which the telescope was pointing

Information received by radio telescopes is recorded on punched tape and passed to a computer, which does about 250,000 sums for each observation. (Keystone)

when radio signals were above or below a certain strength.

The machine, of course, does not talk back its answers but prints them in the form of figures on a long strip of paper. These figures might be meaningless to anyone who did not know what to expect, but without them the work of the Big Dish could hardly be carried on.

8

Looking at Outer Space

Within the past few years, radio astronomers have been locked in an argument as to which of two theories is right. According to one theory, the universe that we know must have started with one colossal explosion, a "big bang." The "big bang" would have occurred when a monster atom, of a substance so dense that a cubic centimeter of it would weigh 100 million tons, exploded and expanded. According to this theory the expansion has continued ever since.

This theory would help to account for the fact that the galaxies in the remote reaches of space are known to be traveling faster and faster away from us and from each other. According to the "big bang" theory, all the galaxies will continue to move away from one another at such a speed that they will eventually be isolated from and invisible to each other, and at a distance of 10,000 million light-years their speed might be too great for there to be any radiation at all.

The second or rival theory, known as the "steady state" theory, holds that although some galaxies are dying off, new ones are being formed continuously from clouds of star dust, so that in the long run the universe stays basically unchanged.

These theories are intelligent guesswork, for we are still in the dark as to how our own solar system was formed.

It seems almost certain that the sun, and the planets circling around it, have a common origin. Compared to the rest of the universe, they are a snug little family, relatively close to one another. The sun, for example, revolves in the same direction as the planets, and the planets and the earth move around the sun in orbits that are almost circular and nearly in the same plane. It seems unlikely, therefore, that Mars, Venus, and the rest arrived from outer space.

The theory in fashion at the moment is that the planets were formed from clouds of dust particles and gas. Perhaps the clouds from which the planets were formed could have started as rings split off from the main body of the sun as the sun shrank away from the clouds surrounding it. Probably the dust was at one time thick enough to cut off all the heat from the surrounding gases. As a result, the gas would have condensed around the dust particles in the same way as fog forms around dust particles on a cold day. Eventually snowballs of a kind would begin to form, which, as they grew, attracted more and more rocks and dust to them. Later — as the dust cleared — the earth, as one of these snowballs, began to feel the heat of the sun and also became still hotter through the force of collision with other meteors and other minor planets attracted toward it.

One puzzling thing, however, is that according to this theory the separation between the sun and the cloud of gas must have taken place at an early stage in the sun's life, before its really hot stage had been reached. Yet, the earth and the planets contain elements that must certainly have been formed from hydrogen gas under the kind of heating conditions that are true of the interior of a star in its later stages (for stars appear to have a life story, a youth and an old age).

Light from the stars is really gaslight. It shines when the gas, hydrogen, is converted into helium, under heat and pressure in the same way — but much more slowly — as the hydrogen in an atom bomb.

During this process the star maintains a kind of balance. The force of the chemical action that blows outward from the star balances the inward attraction of the various parts of the star for each other.

But this balance is a delicate one. If the star is too small, though it may be hot, it won't manage to light up. And if it is too large, the action may proceed so quickly that it breaks up. What happens is that the core shrinks and becomes hotter and hotter until the temperature is so high that the helium itself is pressurized into forming new and heavier substances such as carbon and iron — releasing more and more energy. Eventually the forces pushing outward from this big star overcome those holding the star in; the star then bursts and is known as a nova or supernova.

If we assume, however, that the star has an untroubled life story, it starts as a hot star shedding a bluish or violet light, and as it grows older, its light grows redder and the surface temperature falls. Stars in the early stage of their development can have a surface temperature of about 30,000 degrees Centigrade, whereas the sun, a medium heat star, measures about 6,000 degrees Centigrade at the surface.

But these explanations on the possible origin of the sun and the solar system take us only a short part of the way in our search for the life story of the universe.

At the time this book is being written, neither the "big bang" theory nor the "steady state" theory has been proved right or wrong. There is no past experience that can help us to guess the way in which the universe was formed or what it may become. But each side, with the aid of both radio and eye telescopes, is constantly assembling ammunition in support of its own arguments.

One approach — that of the "big bang" boys — has been to watch the movements of the galaxies today. From their present speed it is possible to work out that a long time, possibly 9,000 million years ago, they were relatively close together. But the "big bang" would almost certainly have taken place many thousands of million years earlier still, and what happened in the meantime remains a matter of guesswork.

For the "steady state" boys, the main interest is to see

if they can observe any changes taking place in galaxies that would show whether, in fact, new galaxies are developing as old ones die out.

Until a few years ago, the main evidence came from the giant 200-inch optical telescope at Mount Palomar. This, as we have seen, can penetrate a distance of 6,000 million light-years and, according to astronomers, should be able to pick out at least 100 million different galaxies.

Many of these have already been photographed and even classified according to their shape — most being of the spiral type. So far, so good. Some astronomers suspect that the disc-shaped galaxies are really spiral galaxies whose spiral arms have been brushed off during their lifetime in the sky. But no such process has so far been detected, and if there is one, it is happening too slowly to be observed in any one galaxy.

One could, of course, assume that the galaxies nearest to us are relatively new galaxies, whereas those on the edge of outer space that are receding faster and faster from us are the old ones. Certainly the light from these more distant galaxies is really light from the past. For example, the light reaching us from the sun takes eight minutes to get to the earth, and therefore, when it arrives, we are really seeing sunlight that is eight minutes old. Similarly, in looking at Alpha Centauri, which is four and a third light-years away from the earth, we see the star as it was four and a third years ago. And the 200-inch telescope at Mount Palomar, when tracking stars at its outermost range of 6,000 million light-years, sees stars as they were 6,000 million years ago. But there does not so far appear to be any clear difference between the galaxies near to us and those farther away. And as long as there are limits on the distance we can see, we shall have only a very imperfect knowledge of galaxies that were formed perhaps far, far earlier.

You may ask how it is possible to tell, apart from the Doppler effect, that those galaxies really are so far away. If a star is comparatively close, you can calculate its distance by its position as seen from the earth at two different points in the earth's orbit. This gives us a definite triangle made up of the base (the diameter of the earth's orbit) and the two angles at each end of the base leading to the star.

But this won't do for distant stars because the base line is so small in comparison to the other two sides of the triangle that it is almost impossible to work out dimensions accurately.

Luckily there is another way of going about the job. Scattered about in various parts of the sky are stars called Cepheid variables. These stars behave almost like a beating heart. That is, they expand and contract according to a kind of rhythm, and their light grows brighter and brighter as they contract. (Some Russians reconcile the "big bang" and "steady state" theories by concluding that the whole universe behaves in the same way.)

Hundreds and hundreds of experiments have shown that there is a relationship between the brightness of the light to be expected from a Cepheid variable and its rhythm. Stars with slow expansion and contraction are brighter than those with fast rhythm. Consequently, astronomers, by measuring the rhythm of any Cepheid variable in the sky, can tell what its brightness should be, and by comparing this brightness with what they actually see, they can tell how far away the star is. Cepheid variables are found in many different parts of the sky, and so there are many points of reference for the stars around them.

A similar comparative method is used for stars when there is no Cepheid variable. The light that reaches us from a star is not the same light that leaves the star because of the gases and dust through which it has to pass on its way here. What we see is the apparent brightness of the star. But by analyzing the quality of the light that reaches us, it is possible to calculate what the true brightness should be, and by comparing the apparent brightness with the true brightness, it is possible to estimate the distance through which the light has traveled.

The study of light is one of the most fascinating branches of physics, and this has become more, rather than less, important since the arrival of the radio telescope.

We cannot yet verify the distances of those remote stars or galaxies that we are not able to see. However, strong radio signals come from stars so far away that we can only just see them, and it is reasonable to suppose that a proportion of the other fainter signals are coming from galaxies beyond the range of eye telescopes — galaxies that are getting farther away every second.

If these radio galaxies in outer space continue traveling away from us at increasingly high speed, it should be possible to detect a Doppler shift of radio wave length away from the short wave lengths toward the longer wave lengths.

But the range of radio wave lengths that can be expected from a radio star is not nearly as precise as the range of light waves from a visible star, and at the time of writing no radio Doppler effect has been established. If and when it is, we shall be able to map outer space very much more accurately that at present.

For the moment, however, many, but by no means all, radio astronomers assume — and there is good reason to suppose they are right — that the majority of radio sources untraceable to a visible star are farther away than those that can be traced. And on this assumption they have been preparing preliminary surveys of outer space. And this is where the "steady state" theory comes into conflict with the "big bang" theory, for the "big bang" theorists say that they have found a greater concentration of galaxies in outer space than there are in our regions. This, say the "big bang" supporters, is the result of the "big bang," which has blown these galaxies beyond our range of vision. It follows that galaxies are not being renewed in our area as fast as they are disappearing into outer space and that, therefore, there is no such thing as a steady state.

But the "steady state" supporters say that they can explain this away. They point out that only certain rather peculiar types of galaxies, for example, those in collision, give out strong radio signals, and they argue that these peculiar galaxies tend to be old ones. In between and perhaps nearer (though out of range of eye telescopes), there may be many other galaxies born perhaps from the clouds left behind after a collision of galaxies and incapable of sending out strong radio signals but nevertheless numerous enough to support the "steady state" theory. As yet no one knows the answers, and every time the men on the telescope think that they have discovered enough evidence to prove or disprove the "steady state" theory or the "big bang" theory, the supporters of each side manage to think out some new and ingenious explanation that proves they still have right on their side.

9

Future Prospects

Never has the future seemed more exciting to astronomers. Today the age of space travel has arrived, and men are mapping the safest routes for space ships to reach the moon and the planets in the same way as ancient mariners charted the rocks and shoals of the oceans and the favorable and contrary winds in each quarter of the globe. But instead of hurricanes, space ships have to contend with solar winds that prevail among the electrified gases of the sun (we have noticed their effects on comets). And one day it may be vital to know how to counteract their influence.

The sun sends out torrents of radiation that pour across space and upset both our own radio sets and instruments on earth and that could perhaps also prove deadly to crews of space ships. These solar "sprays" are of two kinds. First, there are the electro-magnetic waves, such as X-rays and the even shorter gamma rays, both of which

126

in large quantities can be harmful to the human body. The X and gamma rays are unable to penetrate far into our atmosphere from the outside and so fail to reach us in any quantity at ground level. But they remain a potential hazard for anyone who leaves the protection of the atmosphere.

Secondly, there are the cosmic rays, which are showers of particles rather than waves in the proper sense of the term.

Few original cosmic rays reach the earth. Many are trapped in the earth's magnetic field in an area between 500 and 15,000 miles up occupied by the inner and outer Van Allen belts — another big radiation hazard for space travelers. You might perhaps compare the Van Allen belts to the dangerous area near the shore where there are breakers through which the lifeboat is launched only with difficulty on its way out to sea.

Other cosmic rays are deflected toward the magnetic poles of the earth (the earth, as we have seen, is really a big magnet) and give rise there to secondary effects such as the aurora borealis. Other cosmic ray effects can be traced by instruments sent up in balloons or in certain circumstances, even at ground level.

Obviously the space ship must steer a course to avoid, as far as possible, the cosmic rays that are more penetrating even than gamma rays and that could be even more harmful in large quantities. Some cosmic rays, we know, are sent out by the sun because the aurora effect is particularly noticeable soon after certain types of sun flare.

But not all cosmic rays come from the sun, and it is difficult to trace them back to their source with any degree of accuracy, since their paths are bent by the earth's magnetism. At one time it was hoped that cosmic rays could be traced like meteors by the trail of electrified air and radiation left behind them, but so far no traces have been discovered.

It is possible, however, that gamma rays may provide the clue. Gamma rays are believed to be generated by gases under enormous temperature and pressure in much the same way as the sprays of cosmic ray particles. But gamma rays, unlike cosmic rays, are not bent or deflected in a magnetic field and so can be traced along a straight line back to their source.

Until recently it was impossible to trace them because gamma rays did not penetrate far enough into our atmosphere. Only now, in the satellite age, have we been able to make a proper survey of gamma rays by installing a receiver on a satellite flying between 300 and 700 miles above the surface of the earth.

The U. S. scientists undertaking this survey came up with a very ingenious receiver designed to turn head over heels ten times a minute so that it scans a section of the sky every six seconds. Once again we have here a telescope with which no one directly sees anything. Instead of having glass lenses, it is packed with crystals of a kind that send out an electric spark when struck by a gamma ray, and of course a record is kept of the direction in which the receiver was pointing at the time of contact.

The sparks are counted automatically by a register installed in the satellite and the numbers and other necessary information radioed back to ground level. Here an earth-based radio telescope such as the Big Dish, which can follow moving satellites accurately, comes into its own.

By sorting out the gamma rays, scientists may be able to find out what proportion of the cosmic rays actually comes from the sun and what proportion from other parts of the universe — and at what times. The astronomers would feel much happier, too, if they could sort out the different kinds of storms that take place on the sun and if possible forecast the kinds of radio disturbances that take place as a result.

One attempt along these lines was made in March, 1961, when Explorer X, a 79-pound U. S. satellite was hurled into an oval-shaped orbit from Cape Canaveral. Announcing this, the National Aeronautics and Space Administration, or N.A.S.A. for short, explained that Explorer X was designed to make the most extensive study ever attempted of the earth's magnetic fields and the way they affect and are affected by solar winds.

"New knowledge of this environment," the scientists said, "will make it possible to chart flight through the least hostile regions of interplanetary space." At most points, space ships leaving the earth would have to pass through a section of the Van Allen belts. It might sometimes be possible to avoid the Van Allen belts by launching the space ship through an area near to the magnetic poles, where there are gaps in the radiation belt. But these areas, too, become charged when there are sun storms. The object of the survey was to find out as much as possible about the timing and the conditions in the polar gap under different conditions of the sun's activities, so that ships could be launched under the safest possible conditions.

In order to measure the strength of the earth's magnetic field in different areas, Explorer X was equipped with an instrument known as a magnetometer, worked with rubidium vapor. Two other magnetometers measured not only the strength but also the direction of the magnetic fields, while a further device was installed to record the density, the directions, the bulk, and the energy of particles shot from the sun.

One day soon, instruments will be planted on the moon. These will be able to send back information on radio sets whose batteries will be powered by rays from the sun. And what better instrument could there be for receiving messages from the moon or the planets than the Big Dish?

One day, too, it will be possible to recover not only radio waves from the moon but also the instruments that send them, and one can imagine the return signal being sent out from a radio telescope and the satellite being guided by it back to earth.

The recovery of instruments offers us the first chance of a definite answer to the question of whether any form of life exists outside this earth, for instruments can bring back samples. At first the sampling might be rather hit or miss. The satellite might, for instance, carry a sticky tape that could be shot out or have a vacuum chamber—preset — to open and shut rapidly again when it had sucked in a sample of some kind. It might be a handful of dust or just a gulp of the moon's air; but whatever it might be, it could keep the scientists busy for months. Even if no insects, reptiles, or thistledown had been sucked into the vacuum, there might be bacteria — perhaps of a kind that could be grown and studied in a laboratory for a start — since it might be dangerous to let loose a new kind of bacteria into our world without knowing anything about the diseases it could bring.

It would be unwise to expect living things elsewhere to be what they are on earth or to conclude that because we could not survive on the gases that surround Venus, for example, it would be impossible for some form of life to exist there. Even on this earth, there are some startling examples of what can be done. It is possible for a form of life to exist in a 10 per cent solution of sulphuric acid and in another unpleasant medium—mercuric chloride, sometimes known as corrosive sublimate. Life can exist under pressures 8,000 times as great as that of our own atmosphere and in temperatures little short of the boiling point.

Of course, it would not be absolutely necessary for a satellite to land on the moon and take off in order to get samples of the moon's atmosphere. It could pass close to the moon and take air samples without landing. And the Big Dish could be useful as a homing device even if no landing were made.

Meanwhile, Sir Bernard Lovell has been working on

plans to increase existing facilities at Jodrell Bank and the external frequency range by making an oval version of the Big Dish. Lovell's oval radio telescope would measure 150 feet across and, like the Big Dish, would be fully steerable. Its curves could focus rays on the radio aerial in the same way as the Big Dish. Lovell's theory is that an oval dish will be easier to manage than a round dish, since if the long part of the oval lies along the horizontal axis, then the dish won't catch the wind so much when it is turned sideways. The construction costs for a highly accurate instrument would, in turn, be lower, since it would not need so much strengthening.

At first sight it seems surprising that Lovell should consider working with anything smaller than his present Big Dish, but if the small model is successful, then he would be in a position to press for something larger.

And here we come up against the most difficult of all the problems that the modern scientist has to face — namely, the human problem. In the Middle Ages the scientist could be a man apart. If he had enough determination and singleness of purpose to separate himself from his fellow men, enough intellectual honesty not to take for granted the beliefs of his age, and health enough to allow him to put in long periods of research at irregular hours, then he could be said to have the main qualifications for success.

But today there are few one-man jobs in science, and the scientist has to work as one of a team. He can no longer be a recluse or a hermit. He must be able to get along with his fellows. And although it is necessary for him to have an independent mind, yet he must at times take on trust the opinion of scientists in the same team whose experience is greater than his own. He must be able to exchange ideas with specialists in other fields — and finally he must be able to explain himself to people who have little scientific knowledge and almost no idea of the importance of the work he is doing.

He needs this knack in order to convince the government departments and general public that it is worth their while to pay for the expensive machinery and instruments that he requires nowadays for his work.

Moreover, we have now reached a stage where scientific projects have become too expensive to be handled by one single nation. In many cases they have to be undertaken jointly by several governments. So the scientist now has to be a diplomat as well as a good fellow who gets along well with other scientists.

Thus, one can imagine that in the case of someone like Sir Bernard Lovell, it has sometimes been a struggle to decide on the best course to pursue in the interests of radio astronomy. Is it better, for example, to spend day after day in London talking to civil servants and politicians, persuading them to spend more money on a really big new telescope? Or is it better to make do with a smaller instrument and use it during the time saved by not taking journeys to London? In Russia, where the scientist gets almost everything he asks for, it might be no problem. In other countries it is different. One can only say that so

far Lovell has succeeded in all tasks — in carrying out
research not only with one team but also with several and
in interesting his own and other governments in the work
of the Big Dish, which in its few years of life has become
one of the modern wonders of the world.

10

Follow That Satellite

The man-made satellites that the Big Dish observes now and then are getting more weird and wonderful almost every month. Already they can "see," "hear," "count," "touch," carry on conversations, and take their own temperature. If only they could smell and taste, they would be almost human.

The Big Dish has a special relationship with the more "intelligent" satellites, or "interplanetary stations" as the Russians call them, because all communications between satellites and the earth are by means of radio impulses sent out either by the satellite or by the command station on the earth below.

Sometimes, particularly in the early stages of its flight, the satellite automatically sends out a continuous stream of "beeps," telling the world where it is. But in the case of a long-distance probe, going, for example, toward Venus, the satellite, as it gets farther away from the earth, be-

Explorer XII, a typical U.S. satellite used for research. The vanes do not unfold until the satellite has reached outer space, where there is almost no air resistance. (National Aeronautics and Space Administration)

comes more and more like a star whose reappearance in the sky can be reliably foretold, and there is no need, therefore, to get a continuous signal from the satellite, whose batteries, incidentally, would run down all the quicker if they were in continuous use. Instead, the ground station can send a radio impulse to switch on the electrical transmitting apparatus in the satellite — and turn it off again, perhaps, after half an hour, when it is no longer required.

A not-so-different system has been in force for years at sea, by which an alarm sounds automatically in the wireless cabin of a ship, even when the operator is not on duty, if the Morse code signal "SOS" is received a certain number of times in succession.

But the satellite, unlike the ship, not only switches on automatically in response to a signal, but it also replies to questions. And space scientists call this question-and-answer process "interrogation."

The simplest kind of answer that you get from interrogating a satellite is a "beep" giving its position. But the men on the ground want something more than a mere "beep." For example, they want to know how hot it is "up there," and they want to find out whether the satellite's batteries are keeping up a good voltage, and so on.

But how is a figure such as 98.4 degrees transmitted from the satellite back to earth? It *could* be done by sending out 984 separate electric impulses or shocks from the satellite, but they would take a terribly long time to count. Or the Morse code could be used. But Morse needs five dots (short signals) or five dashes (long signals) or a mixture of the two to represent each single figure. That's also slow.

What the scientists wanted was a quick and practically foolproof code, easy to send, easy to record, and above all easy to translate at the receiving end for use in calculations. They found their answer in a system of numbers that represents every number by either a "one" or a "zero." This two-symbol method is known as binary numbering.

The fact that only two numbers, "1" and "0," are used makes things much easier for the electronic brains, known as computers, that have to do the calculations. The old-fashioned adding machines — even the electric ones — do their sums with the help of spindles and cogs. Each wheel in an old-fashioned adding machine has to have ten different positions to correspond to the numbers from "0" to "9." But if you have only two numbers, "1" and "0," you can change from one to the other and back again merely by shunting an electric current from one circuit to another, and by using the right type of valve, you can make the change in about one millionth of a second. This is how the computers manage to work so fast.

But how can you represent all numbers by using only the symbols "1" and "0"? First, you must disregard the usual numerical values of "1" and "0" and consider them only as code expressions. It is only coincidence that numerical 1 is represented by the symbol 1. Numerical 2 is represented by "1" and "0" in the form "10." Now, let us examine the binary representation of the usual numbers 1 through 9.

1					1
2				1	0
3				1	1
4			1	0	0
5			1	0	1
6			1	1	0
7			1	1	1
8		1	0	0	0
9		1	0	0	1

A specific numerical value can be given to each binary "1," depending upon how many binary units are included and where the "1" falls. Let's examine the same diagram, but this time including a value for each column.

Numerical value	32	16	8	4	2	1
Number						
1						1
2					1	0
3					1	1
4				1	0	0
5				1	0	1
6				1	1	0
7				1	1	1
8			1	0	0	0
9			1	0	0	1

Number 5 is represented by binary "101." The "1" on the left has a value of 4; the "1" on the right has a value of 1. Added together, they equal 5! (The "0" in the center is a blank indicating no value.)

Let's try one more example — 7. The "1" on the left has a value of 4; the "1" in the center a value of 2; the "1" on the right a value of 1. Added together — 7! And so it can be demonstrated that any number can be represented as a binary using only *two* symbols. Thirty-two would be 100000; 103 would be 1100111. (You can make your own demonstration chart for the binary system; keep in mind that each item in the numerical value line at the top is double the preceding number.)

So, it's not surprising that the satellites send their signals on the "one-zero" principle, or binary system as it is called, for this allows them to work with the greatest speed and simplicity without having to carry cogs and spindles.

And since computers, which digest and compare the information received from the satellite, also work on the binary system, the "ones" and "zeros" received from the satellite can be fed straight into the computer automatically and without a second's delay. The "ones" and "zeros" are passed to the computer on tape with holes punched in varying positions to signify "1" or "0."

So much for figures. In addition to counting, however, the satellite must be able to *describe* what it sees. This means sending *pictures* from the satellite back to earth. These can be ray photographs of the earth taken with infrared rays that penetrate through the clouds. Or they can be photographs of the tracks of rays or miniature meteorites recorded on plates sensitive to light. Or they can even be pictures of instruments inside the satellite itself.

When a picture is to be sent from the satellite, you must imagine the image as being divided by ruled lines into thousands of tiny squares. Each square, in turn, is then looked at or "scanned" by a photoelectric "eye," similar to that of a television camera, and classified as either a black square or a white square, and a signal to that effect is sent from the satellite back to the receiving station. And so a picture is built up out of black squares and white squares. The same kind of thing happens with pictures radioed across the Atlantic for use in the daily newspapers, which, if you look at them under a magnifying glass, can be seen to consist of an arrangement of black dots and white spaces. A black-and-white system of this kind can be worked just as fast as the "one-zero" system already described — so fast that on a television screen you can't really see it happening.

It would be nice if one could reach the same fantastic speeds as are used in television, amounting to thousands of impulses per second, in messages sent to earth from the satellites. Conditions can change very rapidly for an object moving through space at perhaps 18,000 miles per hour, and it is important for the men on the ground to be aware of such changes the instant they occur.

But signals sent at super speeds cannot be picked up unless reception conditions are favorable, and under normal circumstances, 50 or more impulses a second are considered a satisfactory rate of sending for a satellite even in the early stages of its flight, when the signals it gives are relatively strong. Some probes, as they draw farther away from the earth, automatically "change gear" and send fewer impulses per second to compensate for the worsening conditions.

A U.S. Navy 84-foot lattice-type dish used for relaying signals via the moon between Washington, D.C., and Hawaii. It is located on the northernmost tip of Oahu Island, Hawaii. (Keystone)

But this is the area in which the Big Dish comes into its own. For example, a smaller radio telescope, 84 feet in diameter, can interrogate a satellite as far as ten million miles away, but unless effective transmitted power from the satellite is above the 5-watt level, the 84-foot telescope will not be able to pick up the answers. The Big Dish, however, has detected responses from Pioneer V's 5-watt transmitter at a distance of 23 million miles, and if the same probe's 150-watt transmitter had been working fully, the distance might have gone up to nearly 100 million miles.

Thus, it is important for Britain and the United States to go into partnership for tracking control and interrogation of satellites. In 1962, the United States helped Britain with the British "space laboratory" UK1, designed for launching on top of a United States Thor-Delta rocket sent up from Cape Canaveral.

And so in March, 1960, when the Big Dish helped to track Pioneer V under the joint Anglo-American system, American members of space technology laboratories, in their caravan close to the Jodrell Bank telescope, sent out the command signals through the Jodrell Bank radio telescope, telling Pioneer V what to do. The Americans also received the signals detected by the Big Dish and sent this information on to Los Angeles by teletype for use in the computer there. The British, for their part, controlled the operation of the Big Dish and recorded the position of the satellite in the sky, using the information provided by the

Los Angeles computer as a guide to where the satellite ought to be.

On such occasions, Jodrell Bank receives advance figures showing where to point the telescope at each half minute after "lift-off." This is just as well because the speed at which the telescope has to move from one half minute to the next, when tracking a satellite, varies considerably.

Often these figures have to be adjusted, after the satellite has been launched, on the basis of its actual position reported back from Jodrell Bank to Los Angeles and then predicted again by Los Angeles to Jodrell Bank.

On the day appointed for a satellite launching, the Big Dish scientists are ready to receive the first signals from the new satellite. These will be recorded in ink on graph paper like any other radio messages received by the radio telescope, on perforated tape for the computer, and perhaps on live sound tape recorded from the noise of the loud-speaker.

As launching time approaches, messages come to Jodrell Bank over the direct line from Cape Canaveral — "Three minutes to lift-off . . . One minute . . ." and, at last, the final countdown to zero when the satellite takes to the air.

Even after that has happened, ten minutes at least will pass before the probe comes above the horizon of Jodrell Bank and, perhaps, as much as eight hours if the probe is fired southwestward, for example, from Cape Canaveral.

Meanwhile, more messages flood in — "First stage has fired correctly . . . Second stage ignited . . . Second stage

burnt out . . . Third stage ignited." These messages become less vital as the first signals from the U. S. satellite
itself begin to arrive. It is probably still 4,000 miles away
when it first surmounts the curve of the earth separating
it from the Big Dish. Then, after a slight adjustment, the
telescope gets right on target, and a steady stream of
information begins to flow onto the tapes.

As rockets and launching techniques improve, the space
vehicles will be able to carry more powerful sun-charged
batteries and transmitters. But for many years to come, it
will be important to save weight so that probes can travel
as far afield as possible. And as long as this is the case, the
Big Dish will come in handy.

Part of a powerful radio telescope under construction at Nançay in France. This reflector will help to focus radio waves received by another part of the telescope 500 yards away. (Keystone)

The 210-foot radio telescope at Parkes, New South Wales, Australia, which is being used to map the Milky Way from a south-of-the-equator viewpoint. (David Moore, Camera Press, London)

Appendix

Here are some notes on some of the world's radio observatories already built or under construction and on the kind of work they do.

NORTH AMERICA
United States

At least ten universities, including Alabama, Alaska, Cornell, Florida, Harvard, Illinois, Michigan, Ohio, Stanford, and Yale, study radio astronomy. Harvard has a special radio observatory in Texas. Michigan is building an 85-foot dish-type radio telescope, and Ohio has developed an effective combination of spiral aerials.

Associated Universities Incorporated has also undertaken to provide equipment for research in radio astronomy for a group of U.S. universities. A large dish-type radio receiver has been built at Green Bank, West Virginia, and will be used for temperature studies. Its 300-foot diameter makes its even bigger than the Big Dish, but it is not fully steerable and can swing only north and south. A 140-foot fully steerable telescope is under construction on a site nearby, though it has run into some construction difficulties.

Two 90-foot dish-type telescopes ordered by the California Institute of Technology are sited at Pasadena, and a 210-foot dish is to be built at Goldstone, California.

The Vermilion River Observatory, built in a ravine at Danville for the University of Illinois, is a wire-mesh trough 400 feet by 600 feet, which reflects signals onto a horizontal aerial running along above the center of the trough.

The Naval Research Laboratory in Washington works with a 250-foot fixed reflector, a 50-foot steerable dish, and has a larger 85-foot reflector under construction.

In Puerto Rico a fixed bowl, 1,000 feet across with a movable aerial, is being built with help from Cornell University.

Canada

Canada's newest radio observatory is located in the Rocky Mountains at Penticton.

EUROPE

Belgium

Several different types of radio telescopes are in use at the government field laboratory at Humain-Rochefort.

France

A new radio observatory with a 32-piece interferometer has been set up at Nançay, some ninety miles south of Paris. A second telescope, with an aerial fed by two reflectors placed opposite each other, is also under construction at Nançay. It is highly sensitive but not fully steerable. Other radio observatories operate under institutes set up at Meudon near Paris and in Haute Provence, farther south.

Germany

West Germany has radio observatories at Bonn, Freiburg, Kiel, and Tübingen. There is a radio observatory at Potsdam in the Soviet zone of Germany.

Netherlands

The government has set up a foundation for radio astronomy, which is supported by three observatories at Groningen, Leyden, and Utrecht. An 85-foot "dish" set up at Dwingeloo, to the north, is the largest instrument in use there.

United Kingdom

The United Kingdom has two other important observatories apart from the one at Jodrell Bank. Since 1945 the Cavendish Laboratory at Cambridge has specialized in interferometers for determining the position of radio stars, and this work led to the establishment of the Mullard Radio Observatory, where two of the largest radio telescopes in the world are being used to explore the galaxy. The aerial of one of these interferometers is 3,300 feet long, and the other has a moving aerial measuring 60 feet by 200 feet, which runs on rails 1,000 feet long.

At Malvern, the physics division of the Royal Radar Establishment uses two 85-foot dishes mounted on tracks as an interferometer, together with a small 45-foot instrument.

U.S.S.R.

The Russians are using a wide variety of radio telescopes for plotting the positions of radio stars, for observing activity in the sun, and for making other surveys.

The Lebedev Institute in Moscow has a branch in the Crimea stocked with a large number of radio telescopes, including a 100-foot concrete reflector. A newer station at Sherpukhov, fifty miles south of Moscow, already has a 65-foot dish-type reflector and a cross aerial made up of cylindrical trough reflectors. A larger radio telescope, popularly referred to by Western astronomers as the "Red Cross" because its antenna design is similar to that of the "Mills Cross," is under construction there.

One of the most remarkable of the Russian instruments is at Pulkova near Leningrad. It consists of a reflector made up of movable plates, arranged in an arc 500 feet long, that focus radio impulses onto an aerial. The focus of the reflector can be adjusted, though only in a north-south direction, by tilting the individual plates.

The Russians also have an astrophysical laboratory in Armenia with equipment similar to that of the Cavendish Laboratory at Cambridge in Britain.

ASIA

Japan

Japan has five radio observatories, the largest of which, at Tokyo and Nagoya, specialize in the study of the sun's radio activity.

AUSTRALIA

The Radiophysics Laboratory at Sydney has made some outstanding discoveries in various fields of radio astronomy, and its pioneer work continues to be of special value because so few other radio observatories lie in the Southern Hemisphere.

One piece of apparatus designed for studying the sun's activity tunes in to a wide range of radio wave lengths several times every second and records the results on film, thus giving a complete "action picture" of the radio sun.

Another device makes a complete radio map of the sun at any chosen wave length. For this purpose sixty-four dish-type receivers have been set up to work together.

The Carnegie Institute has helped to build a 210-foot dish at Parkes, New South Wales, Australia, to work in conjunction with the Leyden Observatory on mapping the structure of the galaxy.

Australia is also the original home of the "Mills Cross."

Index

Numbers in italics indicate illustrations.